CONTENTS

BUCKINGHAM PALACE

The Royal Scottish Agricultural Benevolent Institution was founded on 7 April 1897 to help elderly, distressed, disabled and infirm Scottish farmers and their families. It was the product of an initiative by Scottish farming community leaders to counter the serious poverty experienced by many farmers on retirement and it coincided with the Diamond Jubilee of my ancestor, Queen Victoria.

Since then, the Institution, with its entirely voluntary funding, has unobtrusively helped many thousands of farming families throughout the country. Today it cares annually for more than 400 individuals who are or have been in agriculture, fish farming, horticulture, estate work or forestry.

The Objectives of the Charity are unique and the essential, practical help which it provides ensures that the daily lives of Beneficiaries are made easier. Through its efforts, worry about daily living expenses is diminished and quality of life improved.

I am proud to be associated with the Royal Scottish Agricultural Benevolent Institution. I congratulate and thank all Subscribers for their work and their support and wish them and our Beneficiaries good fortune in this very special year.

ELIZABETH R

April, 1997.

Drumlanrig Castle
Thornhill, Scotland. DG3 4AQ
(0848) 30248

7 April 1997

This Centenary publication provides an excellent opportunity for praising those who have worked so hard to ensure that the RSABI should prove its worth.

There are many actively working for it today, whose ancestors, like my own, had the vision to start it from scratch. In those days there were no state benefits to help farmers who fell on bad times, but even today, with much higher living standards, these can be sadly inadequate.

In recent years, we have spread our net more widely to encompass others besides farmers whose living has been on the land. With our dependence upon voluntary giving, we rely on the goodwill and initiative of our supporters, spread all over Scotland, to locate those in need and raise funds to achieve our aims.

There are very many names past and present on the lists of Honorary Vice Presidents, Trustees and the Council to whom one would like to pay tribute, but there are just two I would wish to salute here – Miss Midge Ritchie Hay, Organising Secretary, 1966 to 1986, and our director Ian Purves-Hume, who is launching us into the next 100 years with energy and determination.

The Duke of Buccleuch and Queensberry, KT

THE ROYAL SCOTTISH AGRICULTURAL BENEVOLENT INSTITUTION
A Short History
Tony Dalton

The Minutes and Reports of the RSABI provide a fascinating record of the founding and history of the Institution. The early volumes are leather bound and written in elegant script, but in 1905 the newfangled typewriter was introduced to the Secretary's office; although easier to read, the pages somehow lose a little of their allure.

I make no apology for quoting at length from successive annual reports, for not only do they illustrate the history of the Institution and farming in Scotland, but the actual words reflect the thinking of the times. Within the volumes are many recurring themes which are as relevant today as they ever were; the difficulties of obtaining funds, the problems of creating awareness of the Institution's aims, and the reluctance of rural folk to admit to the need for help. The work of the Institution is as relevant and needed today as it was a century ago.

The funds raised ranged from the proverbial widow's mite to whole farms; from a few shillings in a collecting tin to thousands of pounds from major events. The Institution's capital base increased steadily from £5,000 in its first year to £100,000 in 1955 to £1,000,000 in 1988 to the record present sum of £4.5 million.

Surprisingly, in the 100 years of our history only six administrators have guided the Institution's affairs. Mr (later Sir Isaac) Connell, SSC, who was largely instrumental in the founding of the Institution; his son Mr (later Sir Charles) Connell, WS; Kenneth M Campbell, WS; Midge Ritchie Hay; Ian Cumming, TD; and the current Director, Ian Purves-Hume.

But to go back to the beginning:

For the last quarter of the nineteenth century cheap wheat from the prairie lands of America and Canada coupled with cheap meat from the pampas lands of Argentina and the lush pastures of New Zealand had been pouring into Britain. Agriculture was in deep depression, although Scotland with its more balanced farming fared better than England.

Even so, in Scotland a tenth of the hard-won arable land went out of production, grain crops fell by 15%, and emigration reduced the farm labour force to 200,000.

It was against this background that on 7th April 1897 a meeting was held in Edinburgh to decide on founding a Scottish Agricultural Benevolent Institution to commemorate Queen Victoria's Diamond Jubilee. The meeting was held under the auspices of the Highland Society and the Scottish Chamber of Agriculture, and present were a large number representing landowners, farmers, merchants, Agricultural Societies and Farmers' Clubs. A similar Institution in England had been successfully disbursing pensions for nearly forty years 'to a great number of distressed agriculturists.'

In the chair was the Duke of Buccleuch, who commented: 'A great many well-behaved, deserving men undertake the occupation of farming land, which is not always a very profitable concern in these days – and however well-behaved and well-intentioned a man may be, reverses, as we know, do occur.'

The meeting resolved to establish 'an Institution to be named, with the approval of Her Majesty, 'The Royal Scottish Agricultural Benevolent Institution,' for the benefit of aged or infirm and necessitous Scottish farmers and their widows and children.' To be eligible applicants had to have farmed for at least 19 years at a rent of not less than £50 a year, be aged 65 for men and 60 for women, to be necessitous, and to have an annual income below £20. Widows and unmarried sisters or daughters of farmers were eligible, but not their sons. Although these parameters were amended slightly over the years, they remained basically unchanged until 1992.

Within a week of the public meeting over £1100 had been subscribed, a considerable sum when agricultural wages were below £10 per year. An account was opened with the Bank of Scotland, who have remained bankers to the Institution to this day; and the draft constitution was revised. Not bad going for a week.

By the end of the month the Duke of Buccleuch was elected the first President, and subsequent Dukes have held that office successively. Directors were appointed, and Mr Isaac Connell, SSC, designated as Secretary, a post he held with distinction for 38 years. The meeting 'agreed to invite a large number of Peers, Noblemen, Members of Parliament, Landed Proprietors and other Influential Gentlemen to accept office as Vice-Presidents.' They were clearly successful, for the first annual report shows as Vice-Presidents 2 Dukes, 2 Marquesses, 9 Earls, 4 Lords, 12 Baronets, The President of the Board of Agriculture – and one solitary commoner, H J Younger Esq of Benmore. Maybe other commoners were put off by the fact that 'handsome donations are generally looked for' from the Vice-Presidents!

By the year end the magnificent sum of £5524 11s 9d had been subscribed, and within a year of the inaugural meeting, on 6 April 1898, the first election of pensions was held. From 400 enquiries there were 147 applicants, of whom 36 (24 men, 12 women) 'were in all respects eligible in terms of the constitution.' There being sufficient funds for only 16 pensions of £20 per annum, 20 applicants were held over 'until there are vacancies or an increase in funds.' The pension was paid in two halves, the first at Whitsun, and the second at Martinmas.

A nationwide system of Honorary Local Secretaries and Collectors was soon established, and 'It is hoped that Ministers of all denominations, especially in rural districts, will arrange for the holding of Annual Harvest Thanksgiving Services, and apply the collections to the funds of the Institution.'

The reasons given by applicants reflected a depressing similarity – 'Agricultural depression' and 'Bad seasons, low prices and heavy losses among stock' being the most

Lifting potatoes near Kinyuchar - Kilconquhar - Fife, about 1900.

Clipping at Bourblach, Morar, Inverness-shire, about 1910. The clippers are sitting astride stone and turf clipping stools. The boy on the right will bring the sheep to them.

common. 'Ill health and bad times' often appeared, and applicants were often into their seventies when they applied. The bald statements of 'Father's death,' 'Death of husband' or 'Left totally unprovided for' hid a wealth of stories of hardship and poverty. The Committee must have had a heart-rending time when selecting those to receive pensions, knowing that those they rejected were equally in need.

The Prince of Wales in 1899 said: 'I can only allude for a moment to The Scottish Agricultural Benevolent Institution. It has only been in existence for two years. From what fell from the lips of Lord Mansfield, it is indeed an Institution, though young, which I think is well worthy of your support. Anything that can be done to alleviate the suffering of the Agricultural Class, male or female, deserves our sympathy and philanthropic efforts. I need hardly say it will give me great pleasure, if I may do so, to give a donation of £50 towards it.' In 1901 the patronage of King Edward VII was obtained, the word 'Royal' was added to the title, and the patronage of each succeeding sovereign has been continued.

In the early years the Directors correctly took a conservative view about expenditure, restricting the number of pensions well within the income received. But ten years after its founding, in 1907, the Institution had capital of £10,339, and an income of nearly £2,563. £1240 was disbursed along 67 pensioners, and such were the funds that the Directors decided to award a further 18 pensions.

Naturally it was some years before the Institution received its first legacy, which was for £250 in 1907. Since that date very considerable sums have been received, ranging from £9 9s 8d, the sole estate of a widow, herself a beneficiary, to the magnificent gift of the farm belonging to Mr James Turnbull of Drymen, which raised over £300,000. Legacies continue to remain a vital part of the Institution's fund-raising, and provide an essential source for future work.

The Old Age Pensions Act of 1908 led the Directors to comment: 'Some people may imagine that because the Act provides Pensions, ranging from 1s to 5s per week, to certain persons over 75 years of age, there is now little room for the Institution.' They went on to point out that not only was this sum barely adequate, but many persons under 70 were also in need. The Directors were to make a similar comment in the 60s regarding a similar attitude to the Welfare State negating the need for the Institution.

By 1914 agriculture was just beginning to pull out of depression, and this is reflected by the fact the RSABI had capital of nearly £16,000, and disbursed £1948 to 94 pensioners. The Directors would have been less than human if they had not recognised that war is good for farming, and they urged that 'no effort be spared to maintain the income of the Institution, a result which ought not to be difficult seeing the agricultural classes who mainly support the Institution are not likely to suffer so severely through the War as other classes of the community.

At the end of the war the Institution's capital had increased yet again to £19,187, and the number of pensioners to 117. The pension remained at £20 per annum, with £30 for married couples. The immediate post-war years saw a massive change in land, for many estates were sold, crippled by the pre-war depression, and often compounded by the loss of sons and the resulting death duties. Many tenant farmers who had been canny with the proceeds of the war years were able to buy their farms, and within a few short years two-fifths of Scotland changed hands.

There was a short post-war boom, then in 1921 the government repealed the Corn Production Act, which had guaranteed minimum crop prices, and once again agriculture lurched into depression. Surprisingly, throughout the Twenties there was a steady improvement in the Institution's affairs, and much friendly rivalry between the counties as to who could collect the most money. Mr George Myles of Dundee consistently headed the list by appointing a collector for every parish in Forfarshire. 'He then obtained a valuation roll, and supplied each collector with that part of the roll for his or her parish, with a request that each landlord or farmer whose name appeared thereon should be called upon to subscribe. Thus the collectors are able to see at a glance the names and addresses of all likely subscribers in their parishes, and duplication or omission are avoided.' Such a system would work as well today as in 1924!

The letters from the Twenties are, sadly, little different in content from those received nowadays in our much-vaunted Welfare State. Then, as now, there are always folk, who through no fault of their own, are in hardship. Typical are the following:

'I do assure you I feel very grateful for my pension. It has been a great blessing to me. Indeed I don't know what I would have done without it. My sister also feels very grateful for hers, and would have written to tell you, but I am sorry to say her memory is greatly impaired. We are both getting old . . . I was 95 years of age on April 9th, and my sister was 85 on May 10th.'

(2) 'Doubtless I am one case in many, but if the subscribers to your Society understood how much good they really did to those deserving of such relief, and how our anxiety and care for the future were lessened, they would not consider their subscriptions misspent, but rather be proud to think they had done something to alleviate the misfortunes of their more unfortunate brothers and sisters.'

(3) 'I can say it has been and is a blessed Institution for me. It is freeing me from all anxiety about my rent as well as about other things. If it had not been for the Institution I would have had neither a roof to cover me nor bread to eat.'

(4) 'I hardly care to think what would have become of me in my infirmity, but for the generosity of the subscribers to your Institution. I may add that I was a regular subscriber in my more prosperous days.'

The first radio broadcast was made in 1928, and at intervals thereafter: 'While the amounts received as a result of these appeals have not been large, they have served to publicise the work of the Institution, which is still insufficiently known in many parts of the country.'

By 1930 the country was in the grip of a general depression – in some areas farmers could hardly give away their crops. In the North East land sold at £10 an acre, and estates bought in the post-war boom were selling at less than a third of their cost. Although the Institution's capital had advanced to over £37,000 the demands upon it increased.

'Agricultural depression has obliged many farmers to leave their farms after they have lost all or nearly all their capital, and after many years of hard work. This, of course, not only affects the farmer, but also his women-folk who have been dependent upon him, and accordingly it is regrettable that the claims on our funds have been increasing, and are likely to increase further. This year we have as many as fifty-nine applicants all being eligible, aged, or infirm and necessitous persons connected with agriculture, whereas we cannot give more than twenty-five pensions among the lot, in addition, of course, to continue to pay the pensions hitherto awarded.'

Conditions improved marginally, aided by subsidies for liming and draining, the reintroduction of a minimum wage, and minimum prices for grain. It took the seriousness of war with Germany to provide the final impetus to agriculture, but once the danger was evident the results were rapid and positive. Output increased dramatically, for the lessons learnt from the Great War were augmented by science and new machinery – nearly 4,000 tractors were imported from America alone.

At the Annual Meeting on 6th May 1940 the Directors reported: 'Last year reference was made to the depression from which Agriculture was then suffering, but today the dislocation of war is added to the difficulties of an Institution such as this. The diversion of activities into channels connected with war service in various forms, the black-out, shortage of petrol and the abnormally severe winter, which in many cases delayed the visits of our collectors, may all be cited in explanation of the drop in income from collections this year. But the money is needed as never before, and there is another side of the picture. Farmers are still experiencing great difficulties, and we hope that they realise that the importance of their industry is recognised by the Nation in war-time, and will not be forgotten when Peace is once more restored. They belong to an industry which has frequently been neglected, and has suffered from great vicissitudes. They have, however, despite all difficulties, always maintained their support for this Institution which does so much to assist those who have become destitute in old age. The pensions mean a great deal in the provision of the actual necessities of life to the pensioners, but, in addition, there is one thing the pensions do, which to many people may appear as more important, and that is to maintain in the mind of the recipient that feeling of independence which has so long characterized the Scottish people. There is a vast difference between public relief so widespread today – and payment from a fund maintained voluntarily and to which the pensioners have so often contributed. It is in the maintenance of this spirit of independence that the Institution is justified, and it is with confidence that farmers are asked to continue their support, even in these difficult times.'

Farmers heeded the plea, and by the time of the Institution's Golden Jubilee in 1947 the capital fund stood at over £66,000. The success of the Jubilee appeal enabled the waiting list to be eliminated, and pensions to be increased from £20, at which they had stayed from 1898, to £25 or £40 for married couples. Not for the first time the Directors desired 'to record their great appreciation of the untiring efforts of the organisers and contributors whose efforts have been expended so freely in support of the appeal. Those who have supported the Institution so generously have every reason to be gratified in knowing that the object of raising pensions has been achieved as a result of their assistance.'

In May 1961 the Institution took over from the Scottish Office the running of the Scottish Women's Land Army Welfare and Benevolent Fund. The Fund then stood at £7,548, and the Institution continued to award grants to former members of the service; or to women who had been associated with agriculture in Scotland over a period of years. The grants were not in the nature of annual payments, but were awarded to meet special circumstances such as illness or financial stringency. (The fund being so small, the Institution now awards the income annually to all those former Land Girls on their register – about 30).

The following 10 years saw a steady increase in the Institution's funds and activities, and by 1957 funds stood at £118,186, and income exceeded £8,000. The waiting list was eliminated, and the pensions were £30 for single pensioners and £50 to married couples: 'while still comparatively small . . the pensioners find the income enables them to get something more than the bare necessities for survival.'

In 1966 the running of the Institution required a change from the system whereby the Secretary and Treasurer's law firm administered its affairs. Midge Ritchie Hay was appointed Organising Secretary, and her article 'One Score in the Century' appears later in this book, and fully describes her role. At that time funds stood at over £150,000, and there were 313 pensioners being assisted.

Adam Jack, farmer in Forter, Glen Isla, Perthshire, late nineteenth century.
The thatched house behind is gone and the castle has been restored.

The following year Sir Charles Connell retired after 31 years as Secretary and Treasurer; in 1936 he had succeeded his father, Sir Isaac Connell, SSC, who had been largely instrumental in the establishment of the Institution. In recognition of his outstanding contribution to the RSABI Sir Charles was elected an Honorary Vice-President and Life-Director. His place as Secretary was taken by Kenneth Campbell, WS, who for over twenty years guided the affairs of the Institution, and who sadly died in office, February 1989.

In their report for 1968 the Directors made the point that 'We may tend to shrug off our moral obligations to those whom a farming life has given a raw deal by pointing to the Welfare State, but the little extras which the Institution provides make all the difference to a border-line existence . . . We should bear in mind that there is a vast difference between state allowances and payment from a fund maintained voluntarily and to which the pensioners have so often themselves contributed. The continuing work of the Institution demonstrates that the farming community cares about its less fortunate members, and it is with confidence that farmers are asked to continue their support, and perhaps give additional help.'

1972 saw The Royal Scottish Agricultural Benevolent Institution celebrating its 75th anniversary, which coincided with the Silver Wedding of Her Majesty The Queen, the Institution's Patron. In commemoration of these two events the pensions were raised to £40 and £65 for single and married pensioners respectively, and a £10 bonus awarded for the Queen's anniversary.

Five years later, in 1977, funds stood at over £209,000, and income was in excess of £32,000. Yet the Directors had to repeat their message of 1968 when they commented: 'It cannot be too strongly emphasised that our help is still very necessary for many elderly folk, and we earnestly seek the assistance of all in keeping the Institution advised of any thought to be in need of assistance from the funds. Inflation . . . can quickly erode any increase (in state benefit), and the escalation of heating and lighting costs alone – and in particular their effect on the housebound infirm and the over-eighty age group – still gives cause for concern. With this in mind the Directors have also made provision for our "over-80s" to receive a double pension which, it is hoped, will go some way to greater comfort in the forthcoming months. For those marginally above supplementary benefit level, there is still no type of state aid available for winter warmth, and the greater proportion of household expenditure now required for food still leaves many of the aged perplexed.'

Two years later, in 1979, the annual report stated: 'The closing months of this past year have, without doubt, been the most difficult years in living memory for Scottish agriculture. 'Yet although subscriptions were down, the Institution received the greatest sum in legacies in its history enabling it to continue making additional payments to the "over-80s." The bequest of his entire farm to the RSABI by James Turnbull of Drymen – an agricultural college graduate with special interests in animal genetics and stock rearing – has surely left a lasting reminder of his concern for the welfare of persons connected with farming.

1981 saw a major change for the Institution when it moved its headquarters out of Edinburgh to a house at the Ingliston Showground. ' . . . since its inception the Institution has occupied accommodation provided by the Secretary or his legal firm. Although this is no longer the case, the Board look forward to a continuance of the help and guidance given by our present Secretary – Kenneth M Campbell, WS, and remembers the signal service rendered by his predecessors, Sir Charles Connell, WS, and his late father – Sir Isaac Connell – who was concerned with the founding of the Institution.'

It might have been thought that with the Welfare State demand for the Institution's support would steadily diminish, but the message from the Directors in 1983 was in similar vein to that given by their predecessors in 1908 following the introduction of a (very) limited Old Age Pension: 'Although it now appears to have become established Government policy to revise rates of state retirement pension and other benefits annually to compensate for cost of living increases, it has not gone unnoticed that many face problems in understanding their entitlements. Evidence of the Society's help is demonstrated by the innumerable expressions of appreciation which are received from grateful recipients, for it must be recognised the Institution not only raises and distributes funds, but assists all their beneficiaries and would-be applicants for help with guidance on statutory aid. This very necessary communications link requires to be maintained or our degree of effectiveness would be diminished. Those who may be eligible for specific allowances cannot fully comprehend the many conditions in respect of entitlements, while the most recent difficulties experienced by the changing of benefit payments from DHSS sources to that of local authorities have caused some bewilderment. The needs of our disadvantaged elderly ought to receive the most sympathetic treatment from both statutory and voluntary sources.'

Quotations were given earlier from some 1924 beneficiaries, and the content of letters sixty years later show little difference:

". . . when I was farming and subscribing, (I) never thought I would require to call upon the Institution for help,. Now that I and my wife are receiving such help, we want the Directors to know of our gratitude."

"If only we had the energy and wherewithal to personally thank everyone who works so hard to let us know that we are not forgotten. They do it in such a useful way."

"As heating costs seem to have increased so much in recent years, the assistance is of great help to me. As the 'auld wife' said, 'I felt like having a guid greet' when I opened the letter which contained another cheque. Please tell everyone of my heartfelt thanks."

When Midge Ritchie Hay retired on 7 October 1986 after 20 years of service to the Institution, her place as Organising Secretary was taken by Ian Cumming. At Midge's retirement funds stood at over £916,000, and the Institution had an income of some £110,000; this enabled payment of an average £305 to 252 pensioners. Two years later, thanks partly to legacies and partly to excellent advice from the Institution's advisers, Peter Ensor and Messrs. Laing & Cruickshank, funds stood at over £1 million.

Some ninety years after the founding of the Institution the President of the National Farmers Union of Scotland wrote: 'Certainly, we have entered an era of uncertainty which few of us in farming today have experienced in the past – but Scottish agriculture is not on the edge of an abyss, and it does have a successful future. What is true, however, is that the casualty rate has significantly increased and as an industry and as a people with a record of caring and giving we need to ensure that we have the means to alleviate hardship and distress.'

Ian Cumming, TD, became Organising Secretary in 1986, and presided over initial moves to update and modernise the Institution. He was a meticulous accountant, a conscientious administrator and a caring and sympathetic gentleman, and his sudden death shortly after retirement was a sad loss.

The present Director of the Institution, Ian Purves-Hume, took up office in 1990, and in his first report said: 'Three essential elements contribute to the success of a charity such as the RSABI:

—Beneficiaries
—Voluntary support
—Fund-raising

These members of the WW1 Women's Land Army have adapted their uniforms to Borders fashion with their bondager-style heid-handkies and straw bonnets.

Of these, the ability to identify the need and to find and recruit beneficiaries is fundamental and the most important. It is through success here that our volunteer helpers are best motivated and persuaded to give freely of their time and talent. Gathering money is important but must be of a lesser priority; it will follow from the level of success achieved in the first two elements. If you don't have beneficiaries, how can you ask for help (either in terms of time or money) convincingly.

Beneficiaries are the life blood of the Institution and the quest to increase the number of people we help is never ending. I would like to ask all who read this Report and who have the best interests of farming and the RSABI at heart, to tell us about individuals in difficult circumstances whose plight might be eased by help from the Institution. Please don't hesitate to write, telephone or call – there will always be a positive and sympathetic response.

Finally, we desperately need to increase our voluntary support throughout the country. Any individual who has a sympathetic interest in the welfare of the agricultural community and who feels that he or she would like to become more actively involved, please do get in touch, for there is much work to be done.'

That year there were 250 beneficiaries, a number which had remained static for some years. They each received up to £440 in additional income, as well as having their television licence paid. To commemorate the 90th birthday of her Majesty The Queen Mother all beneficiaries also received a hamper of foods.

A policy of beneficiary visiting was started, and Liz Brash's calls were universally welcomed. In some cases she was able to subsequently remove a cause of anxiety, and occasionally her visits led to identification of other causes of hardship in which we have been able to help. (A report from Liz appears later in the book.)

Since its inception the Institution had had a fairly narrow remit as to whom it could help, ie, farmers, their wives and daughters. Sons or farm workers were excluded, and it was felt by many that a broader remit was needed which would attract stronger support from the public to the RSABI. Equally the way the Institution gave money needed scrutiny, as annual pensions were not necessarily the best use of funds; for example, for some folk the pressure would be eased if the TV or road fund licence was paid. For others help with funding additional fuel, respite care, or crisis grants might all be of more benefit to a greater number of beneficiaries.

Discussions on the way forward and the necessary amendments to the Constitution took considerable time and effort, and proposals were eventually put to the AGM in 1992, where they were passed unanimously. Gone were most of the existing constitutional restrictions, to be replaced by one, broad charitable objective, backed by comprehensive new management regulations. The resources of the RSABI would from now on be available to anyone who is or has been in a rural occupation. Henceforward the RSABI would be a benevolent Institution, not a provider of pensions.

The Principle Object of the Institution was in future to be: 'To provide payments or otherwise afford assistance, to persons who are or have been engaged full-time in agriculture, aquaculture, horticulture, forestry or rural estate work in Scotland, and who are in necessitous circumstances, and their dependants, and also to persons who have served as Honorary Local Secretaries of the Institution.'

The chairman of Council, John M Stevenson, added: 'The RSABI is uniquely placed in having close and effective links with rural communities throughout Scotland and it stands alone in its new, broader and more flexible guise. It is Scotland's rural charity and as such it merits everyone's support.'

Perhaps somewhat surprisingly the quite significant constitutional changes implemented in 1992 did not result overnight in a torrent of enquiries but there has been a steady and increasing volume of new applicants. In 1993, the first year under the new rules, 330 individuals were helped and in the current year (1996) the figure is likely to be over 450. In 1990 about one enquiry every 3 months was the norm; now about 12 are received each month and there is little doubt that the work of the Institution is more widely known especially among community care organisations.

The way in which help is given has been made more flexible, with each application being assessed very carefully on its own particular circumstances and the response tailored accordingly. The RSABI is now more than just a source of material help, for many applicants and beneficiaries it offers an objective and sympathetic listening ear and sound practical advice. The most important operating principle is to ensure the privacy and respect the pride of each applicant.

On 7 April 1997 the RSABI will celebrate exactly 100 years of charitable work. Since its creation in Edinburgh under the joint auspices of the Highland Society and the Scottish Chamber of Agriculture by those wise, prudent and far sighted members of the farming community, from a cautious beginning, it has disbursed more than £2.3 million to over five and a half thousand beneficiaries throughout the country. It would be satisfying to be able to consider that the services of the Institution will no longer be needed as we reach the millennium but sadly, research initiated by the Council indicates that the reverse is likely to be the case.

With the help and support of the whole Scottish community the RSABI will continue to serve those less able and fortunate to the best of its ability and limit of resources throughout a second century.

Told to one editor by an elderly lady: "The stallion used to go from farm to farm covering the mares – now you couldn't do that with a tractor, could you?"

"In 1917-18 there were horses and carts and you got 6 weeks of fine weather for harvest. In those days everyone went to the harvest. Kids helped too. Tea and jammy pieces were brought to the field. We chased rabbits and mice. The thresher was driven by a traction engine and it had to start very early in the morning to get steam up."

BENEFICIARY REPORT 1996
Five Years on – where to now?
Liz Brash

By putting some facts and figures on paper, I hope to give a clearer understanding of the variety and the flexibility of help required to meet the needs of men and women applying to the Royal Scottish Agricultural Benevolent Institution for assistance towards the end of the 20th century. This is especially relevant as the Institution approaches its Centenary and the possible uses of a Centenary Fund are being considered, so that our resources are used to the full to benefit the needs of rural folk into the 21st century.

When I started to work for the RSABI in January 1991, my main aim was to become acquainted with the 240 Beneficiaries being helped at that time. Few of them had met anyone connected to the Institution, so in some cases my visit was awaited with trepidation and I was often greeted with comments such as: "I wondered what you would be like?"! After discovering I did not have two heads, I have always been treated with the utmost kindness and hospitality – more than a stone added to my weight can testify to that! It took me over two years to visit the original number from Shetland to the Solway, omitting the Western Isles. These visits were mainly of a social nature, for me to tell the Beneficiary, in the familiar surroundings of their own home, the many ways in which the Institution wished to be of help. There is always an open door, all matters are treated confidentially and even if it is only for a chat, they should not hesitate to contact the office – which becomes much easier for them once I have visited them in their home.

My report of January 1994 stated that I was on my second/third round of visits and this situation has not changed. I am still on my second/third round of visits for most Beneficiaries, but in some cases I have made many visits, when there has been a crisis or a particular problem that requires monitoring and on-going help. Due to the increase in the number of people requiring help of an on-going nature my second round of visits is becoming more drawn out. Indeed, the first opportunity I had to visit Beneficiaries on Islay and Skye was Easter 1996!

The last two years have seen a considerable change in the nature of my work in a number of areas, but particularly in the variety of problems with which I cope. This can be attributed to various reasons.

a) The present number of Beneficiaries is 325, so there are more people to have more problems – not to mention the 80 or so who receive single grants each year. Many new clients have been made known to us through existing Beneficiaries.

b) The work of the Institution, as a caring organisation, is at last reaching the ears of many other organisations – the Citizens Advice Bureau (CAB), Age Concern, Care & Repair, the Royal United Kingdom Beneficent Association (RUKBA), the Gardeners Royal Benevolent Society (GRBS), the Guild of Aid for Gentlepeople, the Professional Classes Aid Council (PCAC), the Buttle Trust and the Electronics and Electrical Engineers Beneficent Association to name but a few. In many cases we refer Beneficiaries to these other organisations for additional help, or these organisations refer cases to us and we co-operate with them when applicable.

The GRBS and the RSABI help a couple who were market gardeners all their married lives. We introduced them to the GRBS and this organisation accepted them as annual beneficiaries. The gentleman suffers from Parkinson's Disease which caused him to retire early. They are now in their 70's and his condition has deteriorated quite a bit. Their only luxury is their car and keeping it on the road is a considerable expense for them. Over the last two years the RSABI has paid their TV Licence and this year we gave them a single grant towards their car expenses. The GRBS do not pay TV Licences.

The Professional Classes Aid Council (PCAC), the Buttle Trust and the RSABI help a farmer's widow with two teenage children. The farmer died leaving his family with many problems. His wife had contacted the RSABI a number of years before, for help while he was ill. Due to the constitution at that time no help was available. After his death she turned to us again, being in a desperate situation. We accepted her as an Annual Beneficiary and advised her to contact the PCAC and the Buttle Trust – a charity based in Glasgow which helps children who have suffered misfortune in family life due to being deprived of a parent. With the help of the three organisations the family has overcome many problems and can look to the future with some certainty.

c) To many people money is a help but in a lot of cases a listening ear and an on-going interest in their welfare is what is required. The expansion in this type of assistance has been most noticeable in the last two years.

Like the divorced Tractorman, living in a tied cottage, who was unemployed for the first time in 36 years in the industry and who was literally at his wits end, almost suicidal, when a lady in the CAB pointed him in the direction of the RSABI. It was a most unfortunate set of circumstances which had resulted in his having to leave his home and latterly having no telephone. This was a considerable drawback when trying to find a job. He came to the office to use our telephone. We gave him some financial help but, more importantly, we gave him the time and support to successfully find a new job! He was one of the lucky ones! However, like many others, until misfortune befell him he did not know of the RSABI's existence. He will now be one of our main ambassadors!

The lady of 55 who had to take early retirement, after a life-time as a poultry-maid, due to asthma and chronic "bird's disease." Her ill health was aggravated by financial problems through the loss of her regular income. She became very depressed and things were reaching a low ebb for her, until she contacted her CAB who informed her of the RSABI. Working together, the two organisations were able to advise her about benefits she should claim and help her through the bureaucratic maze of form filling. I had a telephone call from her about two weeks ago to say that she has been awarded Severe Disablement Allowance back dated to 1986 when her asthma was first diagnosed! Her appreciation of our help was such that she could not stop saying "you are a great, great organisation!"

d) Due to having a personal contact with someone in the Institution, a Beneficiary is more likely to telephone or write when they have a problem. The type of problem is as varied as are the Beneficiaries. It may be financial. It may be to discuss with someone outside their family whether moving to accommodation for a retired person might be appropriate and whether that would affect their benefit from the RSABI. It may be to write a letter in support of an urgent need for council housing, or it may be as minor as a request for help in completing our Application Form.

A farmer's widow, whose parked car was "written off" by a drunken driver late at night, telephoned us the next day as she needed someone to talk to. She was very shocked and upset and had no family nearby so she telephoned the RSABI for a reassuring chat and to get her worries out of her system!

e) As the RSABI is not part of any local community, anonymity is one of the main benefits which we can offer. No one wishes to publicise their personal affairs and those in rural communities are particularly aware of 'neighbourhood watch' and would not wish to be seen

Iain Campbell plaiting heather rope.   (Courtesy of Margaret Fay Shaw.)

*Feeding the hens. Work was a habit,
even in disability or old age.*

going into such places as the local Benefit Office or the CAB. On the other hand, a friend from Edinburgh visiting can be explained without any problem.

A farmer's daughter, who is a spinster living in a small village, had a debt which originated from the time a few years back when her mother was ill and she ordered clothing and bed linen for her mother's use. She was already a Beneficiary and contacted us for help to agree a repayment schedule with the mail order company. She came to the RSABI because there was no danger of anyone local getting to know her business!

f) The holiday programme, which has come to the end of its third successful year, has made Beneficiaries feel that they are part of a club or family which has all aspects of their life at heart. Many who have gone on the holidays are now firm friends and keep in touch throughout the year. It is also a benefit to me, as my being in personal contact with the holiday-makers for a number of days in a relaxed atmosphere builds up a relationship and a personal contact for them with the Institution which cannot be forgotten.

One of the delights of the holidays this year was a farmer's widow who has suffered two strokes and her fair share of illness during the past few years. Her doctor recommended a holiday. When she arrived she was walking gingerly with a stick. By the end of the week having the morale boost of company and conversation she was a changed person – almost running along the street!

g) Each Beneficiary receives at least two newsletters per year, keeping them up to date with the diary of events and any newsworthy points regarding their welfare. They are encouraged to get in touch if they have any queries regarding this information.

A recent letter from a farmer's widow expressed her gratitude for these communications by saying "It is wonderful to see the RSABI stamp on a letter as you know there is sure to be something good inside!"

I think it is evident that, as well as financial help, many people are requiring help which only our time and effort can achieve. The case of the Tractorman is a very good example of the complexity of some of the cases presented to us. It may be helpful to summarise the cost in time to the RSABI of the help which I have given him to date:-

- 5 visits of 1-2 hours each
- at least 24 telephone calls enquiring about employment
- writing 12 letters
- faxing possible job adverts to 4 newspapers
- composing a job advert and list of previous employment
- generally talking through his problem as he had few friends (mainly due to the unsocial hours his work necessitated) and no relations in the area with whom to share his problem.

This list and examples of case histories show that the type and variety of help given by the RSABI has changed dramatically over the last five years. I feel that flexibility is an essential part of the welfare and advice given by the Institution. This is illustrated by the fact that no one is turned away without being given some offer of assistance or the hope that their problem can be solved by another organisation. There is no evidence to suggest that this need is likely to become any less in the 21st century. Indeed, the continuing problems of BSE and the knock-on effect it may have on the rural work force means that the demand for the assistance provided to the rural community can only increase. Even without this possible cause our work load is still increasing monthly, now reaching the level of at least 12 enquiries a month – we are a victim of our own success – and this is wonderful!

I think it will be evident that the help we provide is no longer restricted to money. The case histories described give an insight into the many areas covered by the RSABI. It is no longer an Institution on a narrow path. Beyond the change in the Constitution in 1992 the organisation has been able to widen its remit to address the many different problems faced by rural people towards the end of the 1990's. Farming and rural occupations will continue to present new problems and crises in the future, and the Institution must be prepared to adapt to these situations. It should be our ambition for the future, to become better known as a compassionate caring organisation which is available to provide help, whatever the crisis. As the only rural beneficent organisation we ought to be well prepared to give counselling or advice when required, recognising that the solution may not necessarily be financial.

I believe this report illustrates the increase in quantity and complexity of support being given to the welfare of Beneficiaries.

Rural Reminiscences
1. A Naughty Boy

"Two vivid memories from school days, both were for punishment. One was from father for coming home with wet feet from jumping the burn and falling in and ruining my boots. It came to a head one night when I came home not only with wet feet but trousers, blazer, shirt, the lot. I had fallen head first in. Having just stripped off my wet clothes when in he walked. I still remember not being able to sit in comfort for a week. He had a big hand.

The other was for being late back to school after lunch. We were playing in a field beside a horse and was having a free hurl so forgot all about time. Our headmaster, Mr McIntosh, soon brought us up to date in no uncertain manner. You sat on the desk, one hand on top of the other above your bare knees so if you opened your hand your knees got it – four of the best. These things seem pretty trivial now but I had the greatest respect for my father and head teacher and know the punishment fitted the crime. Vandalism was unheard of at that time. I think there is a point to be taken here."

ONE SCORE IN THE CENTURY
(From the inside looking out)
Midge Ritchie-Hay

When I joined the Institution in the middle 60s, I already had some involvement with charity administration, although no inkling of agricultural life. Many would have said (and some did) that my chequered career was of little use to the RSABI, but my varied work experience certainly proved to be a considerable asset to me. Having served in the ATS, then spent eight years on public relations in the civil service, I found it necessary to resign and return home to look after the needs of my ailing and ageing parents. The ever-increasing problems they faced during the latter years of their lives helped to give me a greater insight into the difficulties experienced by the charity's beneficiaries.

Previously, all the charity's administration had been handled through the good offices of Connell & Connell WS, with Sir Charles G. Connell WS and Kenneth M. Campbell WS presiding over the day to day running of the organisation. The legal firm's staff, coupled with an army of voluntary helpers throughout Scotland had been maintaining an exemplary routine which must have been the envy of many charitable organisations.

For some time pressure groups and like charities had been pinpointing the problems experienced by certain sections of the community. Their difficulties were not being ameliorated by the expected support of a welfare state. Legislation was already in place to check this criticism and, naturally, a vast majority of the public began to believe the State would automatically cover all contingencies.

It took a great deal of hard work to correct this thinking, and throughout my association with the RSABI one tended to hear such thinking from an unenlightened few. I rather suspect such thoughts still linger in some people's minds.

There were over 300 beneficiaries on the Register in the mid sixties, each receiving approximately £30 per annum . . . a paltry sum by to-day's standards. This was, however, an era before the devaluation of the pound; long before decimalisation of our currency, and well before inflation started to create all manner of difficulties.

Initially, my years were spent within an office next door to Connell & Connell WS, which proved to be most useful. All mail could be received and despatched from a central point, and there was the added advantage of 'picking brains' when I was unsure of which direction one should take with a specific difficulty, especially when it could be seen to have a recurring pattern! Then one also had the occasional assistance of the 'three disciples' (Peter, James and John), young apprentices within the firm who were not encouraged to enjoy an idle moment. They became adept at the despatching of annual reports and other bulky mail shots at certain times of the year.

Our capital was standing at around £150,000 which produced just under £7,000 in interest, and income had to be supplemented through voluntary subscriptions and donations to assist with the disbursement of benefit. The Directors were fully aware of the numbers which ought to be helped, but they couldn't reach the most vulnerable for a variety of reasons. They also wished to increase the awards. We were caring for a generation with uncomfortable memories of the 'poor Laws'; it was not easy to convince them of their rights to certain state entitlements nor allow the charity to provide the help that was possible from the funds. Advertising was costly, word of mouth too unreliable and voluntary contributions were falling. The Board members of the day realised that until greater evidence of financial support

Rucking hay at Corf, Taynuilt, Argyll, late nineteenth century.

An unidentified West Highland paddle steamer, probably in Argyll. The development of steam transport made a big difference to the economy of the Hebrides and the Northern Isles.

was forthcoming, existing capital had to be made to work harder. Our stockbrokers, Laing & Cruickshank were encouraged to keep a closer eye on the investment portfolio, and one of the firm's senior partners (Peter J. Ensor) was made aware of the forward-looking efficient management expected. His friendly and wise advice was much welcomed by the Directors.

During this time, many of our voluntary helpers were experiencing difficulties at first hand. A fair amount of comment was being aimed at the Institution concerning administrative costs, and while it was accepted that donors should demand accountability, such criticism was not necessarily justified. There were costs which required to be faced and absorbed and we were competing with all other charities for an acceptable share of the public purse.

Annual re-assessments of the beneficiaries' circumstances were carried out, with careful note being taken of what additional help might be forthcoming from other sources. All too often there were obstacles to be overcome before people could get the information they required. The Institution had the added complication of trying to assist the rural dweller living in the 'face to face' relationships of a village and not wishing to display hardship, albeit through no fault of their own.

The needs and interests of our elderly varied, and considerable flexibility was required in any approach made when visiting their homes. Transportation and food problems could be the greatest worry to some, the sheer lack of human contact caused anxiety to others. Handicapped husbands or wives were particularly vulnerable; their needs could be intermittent and spread over a twenty-four hour day rather than concentrated into a particular period – the only relief being a few hours in any week made possible through local authority arrangements.

It wasn't easy to set a pattern for visits, especially when one eye remained on what was lying on the office desk. However, I heartily enjoyed the experience and could never decide who received the greater comfort. One was always welcomed with open arms . . . and the inevitable cup of tea . . . and it was humbling to hear the related tales of a former life indicating a hardship no one of my generation or since would be able to correctly comprehend. Naturally, there was always some character whose lifestyle puzzled you and left a lasting impression. Like the retired northern farmer whose wife rushed around to make sure I received the customary beverage. "Why have you never mentioned your wife's existence John? She should be receiving benefit." "Och, there's nae need, she'll get what I think she should hae." Needless to say, the Institution placed the wife on the Register, having confirmed this was no 'bidie-in' likely to contravene any clause in the Constitution.

Our debt of gratitude to all our voluntary helpers has always been recognised but, as was to be expected, their numbers decreased due to the ever-spiralling travel costs and growing pressures associated with modern living. The dual role of the local representative, called upon to maintain a level of support through voluntary contributions while providing a personal link between the farmer of the day and the organisation, was difficult. Two or three visits to a farm may have been necessary before the supporter could be located, several miles might be involved and the contributor be only one name in a book of many. Without wishing to damage such valuable personal links, more direct methods required to be encouraged and even a few of our land owners invited their tenant farmers to add their RSABI support to a term rent cheque in an effort to ease the problem.

I had been blessed with a number of extremely strong, innovative and independent local secretaries all over the country, pioneering and original in thought and utterly individualistic. My task was to 'soak up all the colours in the spectrum', strike a balance, yet not destroy their enthusiasm, which was priceless. The doyen of this team was Miss Anne Batchelor . . . a legend in her lifetime. Despite her many difficulties with business duties, domestic commitments and advancing ill-health, her uncanny ability to diagnose problems and resolve same came about through being constantly on the move. Close involvement with the RSABI throughout her life was an invaluable asset and the positive results of her efforts were a joy to report. Many others – less flamboyant, but equally dedicated – attained spectacular results. Without such faithfulness and energy, many links would have been severed as the years went by.

Where there was a flagging of spirit, I would dash to the appropriate area, and on occasions received my just deserts, like the over-ardent bull released to guarantee my hasty departure. Being stranded on the moors in deep snow nearing midnight and having to be rescued by a van load of flower-power hippies on the lookout for further adherents wasn't amusing either.

To augment the voluntary contributions – which never rose dramatically – fund-raising became a time consuming task, and it was only by staging events around the country that we were able to keep the charity's name constantly to the fore. Many of the farming community would be pressed into service and all manner of commercial enterprises approached to donate prizes for raffles etc. At times there would be such a generosity of spirit, the home garage would be crammed with 'goodies' awaiting transportation to some part of the country. Occasionally, one had to make adjustments to the family home insurance just in case!!

Amongst many projects, I certainly recall our Young Farmers deciding to drive a tractor from John O'Groats to Land's End. I agreed to meet them in Moffat where the Provost was donating an acceptable sum to their 'kitty', and providing a much needed meal for the drivers. South of Abington, I encountered an enormous tail back of traffic with only one lane in operation; inevitable road works were in evidence. Traffic was down to around five miles an hour when it was realised our tractor must be ahead and causing a problem. Fortunately, there was time to use the minor road over the hill to Moffat, and I dashed into the Police Station to apologise for the difficulties we were creating. The phlegmatic sergeant calmed my fears with the encouraging remark that "anything reducing the speed of traffic on the A74 is more than welcome in my book". Needless to say, the tractor duly arrived in the town to an overwhelming reception, but I fear those travelling south were not looking upon our charity in a favourable light.

Our 75th Anniversary was marked by the then Secretary of State for Scotland staging a reception in Edinburgh's Bute House, to which many of our friends were invited. This, in itself, proved to be most invaluable, enabling Directors, Secretaries and local Collectors to get together and compare notes. By now donations were gradually being received in greater numbers and in larger sums, thereby permitting the level of support for our aged to be raised again.

However, it was not until the late seventies that the most notable gift in the society's history could be recorded. The late James Turnbull of Drymen—an agricultural graduate with special interest in animal genetics and stock rearing—left a lasting reminder of his concern for the welfare of persons connected with farming. With the proceeds of his estate a special Trust Fund was established (upon his instructions) with the ultimate capital received (almost £365,000) in order that earned income could be equally divided amongst all the beneficiaries on the Register at the close of each year. Such a gift brought a tremendous fillip to everyone, and was the start of greater and more imaginative forms of assistance being introduced by the Directors. Social work benefits were constantly under review, and it was most necessary that any measure of support being awarded by the RSABI was well within the 'disregard levels' set, yet seen to provide means for items not covered by legislation.

Until the close of the seventies, the administration continued to be carried out from Dublin Street, but the march of time was creating all manner of perplexities. Street parking was almost an impossibility, Directors' meetings couldn't be held without some Board member seeking an excuse to 'feed the meter', and the voluntary helpers found it impossible to visit the office without experiencing unnecessary dilemmas. The Chairman of the day, Sandy Clark, eventually found a most happy solution to our problem. The Royal Highland and Agricultural Society of Scotland's Showground at Ingliston had suitable space within one of its bungalows which offered an availability to supporters hitherto unknown. From the time the office was open, a number of visitors called to find out more about our work, and during the Highland Shows each year, we were in a position to return a measure of hospitality to those who had so kindly looked after us.

The government had recognised a long-overdue need for the up-dating of regulations governing charitable giving, and the Public Charitable Collection (Scotland) Regulations came into force. It was known that the society's activities and achievements were being seen for the first time at District Council level. Quite a few of these authorities had little knowledge of our activities and certainly nothing of our cause, and it was deemed appropriate a 'logo' would assist clear identification of the Institution from the many charities competing for funds. Naturally, there were supporters critical of the inevitable impact on costs, but they tended to be those who preferred to see the tree rather than an entire wood. We were anxious to illustrate our harvest of benevolence, and to the outside world it appeared a suitable symbol.

Coming toward the time of my retiral in 1986 my thoughts naturally turned toward all those friends I had made during my association with the Institution. There were so many people, whose individual efforts may have appeared slight, but their collective endeavours achieved much and overcame many almost insurmountable snags. I had also enjoyed a very friendly association with the Scottish Office, which regularly reminded me of the various returns expected to be lodged. I was always made fully aware of any changes in forthcoming legislation and was always given greatest laxity during the implementation of same while involving voluntary helpers. Then, I had the advantage of Kenneth Campbell's astute legal mind. He was always readily to hand in the interpretation of laws which might apply to the charity and greatly assisted with the up-dating of our Constitution at varying times.

I was no singular spirit but rather one fortunate enough to find a circle of interested and dedicated people, who provided a wealth of ideas, encouragement and support. Together, it was possible to continue the aims of the charity's founders and I was very certain any successor would find a similar state, irrespective of outside influences and changing world patterns.

I found that in the necessary things, there was unity; in doubtful things, liberty; in all things, charity.

From a letter by Ian Cumming
to Directors and Hon Local Secretaries

I think you would like to hear about the day Midge Ritchie Hay retired. It was 7 October 1986, the day of the AGM and 7300 days or thereby after her first with the Institution.

The Trustees and Directors decided to arrange a modest luncheon in her honour. Funds being severely restricted, the organisers could not, as they would have liked to, issue an invitation to everybody. Instead, it was a case of "names out of a hat" to determine the guest list from the very many who over the years have been so loyal to the Institution and so helpful to Midge. Those who did attend not only delighted the Guest of Honour by their presence but also ably represented the many who were not present. His Grace the Duke of Buccleuch and Queensbury kindly presided over the proceedings.

At the end of the AGM, his Grace presented gifts and Midge made a short but very eloquent speech of thanks – thanks which she would have liked to convey personally to each and every one of you, not only for the gift but particularly for all the help you have given her.

What was especially remarkable on a very remarkable day was the fact that, unbeknown to everybody, Midge was nursing three cracked ribs and was, as anybody who has cracked but one rib will know, in considerable pain. This, of course, was typical of stoicism frequently displayed by her. The injury I can confirm was not sustained in the course of having the "best of three falls" with her successor but instead while carrying on a balancing act with a saucepan of mince in her kitchen!

In conclusion I would like to record my gratitude to Midge for the trouble she has gone to in order to ensure a smooth hand over. Nobody could have done more – but then is that not typical of her?

PURCHASE AND TRANSPORT OF 33 CATTLE FROM SKYE TO SELKIRK 1866

	Total
Prices ranged from £1 5/- to £6 2/-	£169 8 0
Personal expenses – train, boat, board, fairs, coach and train home	6 9 8
Expenses of taking home cattle – man 26 days at 3/6	4 11 0
Fare in train and boat returning to Skye	1 2 0
9 Tolls (2/6 to 2/9)	1 3 3
Grass, 19 stops, range 2/6 to 6/6	3 11 6
Other Expenses	2 0 9$^{1}/_{2}$
	£18 18 2$^{1}/_{2}$

Time taken 21 days, total mileage 247.

A quote for 1997 transport for 33 cattle for a similar journey from Skye obtained by RSABI was roughly £1000 – £25-£30 per head. It would hopefully take less time!

WHAT THE PAPERS SAID IN 1897

Mary Singleton

The inaugural meeting of the Royal Scottish Agricultural Benevolent Institution was reported in detail in the Scottish Farmer dated 10th April 1897 and the editorial went on to comment "What a terribly long name." It was a good humoured meeting with some laughter and general applause although many of those present felt they themselves would soon be eligible for assistance in the present economic climate. So what was that climate?

Parliament was debating the wholly inadequate food supplies in the United Kingdom which was heavily dependent on foreign imports. However, "In spite of the efforts of temperance reformers, the Englishman continues to drink his beer and since the repeal of the Malt Tax in 1880 there has been a 20% increase in the production of beer in this country." Maybe the demand was there if only the crops could be produced.

In colleges and around the country, pioneers were certainly attempting to improve output. Professor Wright of Glasgow indicated in a lecture that 281lb of bone meal per acre applied to the hay crop lifted its yield from $31^1/4$ cwt/acre to $33^1/2$ cwt. Basic slag, on the other hand, depressed the yield unless it was applied in conjunction with other manures. An advert for Globe fertiliser claimed that it was composed largely of organic matter and possessed the natural qualities necessary for stimulating luxuriant growth and productiveness. It cost 25/- for a ton with a discount on large quantities. The Permanent Nitrate Co was another company "spreading intelligent ideas about the use of nitrate of soda on turnips and other root crops".

Grass seed cost around 8/- per acre for temporary grass or 15/- for permanent pasture. If you grew strawberries they were probably Paxtons, and potatoes might be Farmers' Glory. For turnips or swedes the varieties to go for were Achilles (resistant to finger and toe), Excelsior or Mungoswells Giant. There had been such a good crop of turnips in the past year that many had only been half eaten before being ploughed in.

By early April 1897 lowground lambing had progressed well and should the weather turn more genial there would be a splendid crop of lambs. There had been a long spell of wet followed by hard frost and heavy snow and the hills which had been green a fortnight ago were now browned with food likely to be scarce. Sheep were in a more satisfactory condition than might be expected in the raw biting wind but the hill lambing was likely to be less favourable than last year.

In the farmer's medical kit he probably had some Red Drench for cleansing ewes and cows. Gaseous Fluid was of use for prostrated cows and Skooro provided a certain cure for scouring calves.

A meeting had been held in Perth to discuss sheep stealing. Meanwhile in Glasgow's Possilpark there was an outbreak of enteric fever from contaminated milk but this, I am pleased to report, was traced to the dairy depot and not the farm of origin. Also in Glasgow, butcher Alexander Gardiner appeared in court on a charge of selling meat which was unfit for human consumption, having been condemned at the abattoir. Since it was only his first offence, he was fined £20 with the option of 60 days in prison.

In an advert for Harrison's reliable rat poison, which was safe for dogs and cats, a farmer claimed to have picked up 150 dead rats. Also advertised were various pieces of machinery including Parmiters patent harrows for mossy pasture and general arable work, Ransomes cultivators and Alpha Laval hand powered cream separators.

In the situations vacant column young gentlemen were easily placed as farming pupils and a first class dairymaid was sought – she should not be under 30 years old. Managers, grieves and shepherds were all looking for work. These adverts cost 1/6d for 24 words and you could get three insertions for the price of two. At the recent New Castleton Hiring Fair there was a large attendance and boys were mostly in demand with wages quoted as follows: Experienced men £11-£13, less experienced £8-£10.10/-, boys £4-£7.10/-, women £7-£11, all for the half year with board.

In Perth, McDonald Fraser had forward 7000 sheep, 900 cattle and 100 cows in their weekly store sale. Cross hoggs sold to 35/-, Blackface grit ewes to 32/6, Leicester gimmers 64/-, cross gimmers 36/6 and half bred ewes to 45/-. Two year old cattle made £16.12.6d, stirks sold to £11, Shorthorn cows to £18.17.6d and Ayrshire to £16. Swan and Sons had similar prices with 2000 sheep and 400 cattle forward.

Top prices for grain at auction were: wheat (64lb bushel) 28/-, oats (45lb) 23/- and barley (57¼lb) 27/6. More general prices for oats were 13/6 to 16/-, barley 16-20/-, wheat 25 to 25/6 and a 280lb bag of oatmeal 25-26/-.

If you wanted to sell your wool, which was at a very depressed price, you might send it to Messrs Ramsay or McLeod who were Glasgow Wool Brokers but you could have it made up into tweed or rugs for your own use by A & J McNaughton of Pitlochry (manufacturers to the Queen) or several other firms.

Horses at stud were mostly Clydesdales, hackneys or thoroughbreds. Popular breeds of pig were Large White, Middle White and Tamworth. Later in the year, at Glasgow, the Royal Highland Show winners included an Aberdeen Angus bull called Prince from Sir George Macpherson Grant of Ballindalloch, a Blackface ram from Charles Howatson of Glenbuck, an Ayrshire bull from Robert Mongomerie of Ochiltree and a Shorthorn called Invader from Mr Peterkin of Conon Bridge.

In 1897, it would seem, the weather, crime in the countryside, food safety and traceability were all factors which beset us. A huge market awaited increased production giving plenty incentive for improvement of crops and livestock through genetic engineering and combating disease . . . of course that was a hundred years ago.

With thanks to Mr and Mrs Drew Adam.

Horse and cow drilling on a croft in the Rothienorman district of Aberdeenshire, late nineteenth century. The cow's collar opens to get it over her horns and is shaped to keep her windpipe free. Although cattle were going out for ploughing in most districts in the late eighteenth century, that use survived in Galloway, Buchan and the Northern Isles into this century.

A CENTURY OF SCOTTISH FARMING

Gavin Sprott

The rural Scotland of a hundred years ago is not just a distant place: it has passed beyond living memory. In a general way we know what happened, and with the wisdom of hindsight, we may sometimes think we can understand better than people did at the time why things happened. But to catch the flavour of a past age, to have the sense of a world where peoples' values and expectations in life were just different, that is a much more elusive thing. Most history is a tribute to documentary sources, writing breeding more writing. Reality in the form of spoken history can be much more startling.

I recall a story told me as a child by Mairi Smith, one-time postmistress at Ballintuim in Strathardle. As a young woman she had been schoolmistress on the island of Taransay off the west coast of Harris, during the 1920s. Then she had known a certain *Raonaid Mhor* – Big Rachael. Rachael had been born on one of the nearby islands, but remembered when *na saighdearan* – the soldiers as she called them – came to evict them. It was a cold spring day, with some snow still lying. Her mother was about to give birth, but the eviction went ahead. They carried her mother down towards the shore in a blanket, but in the shelter of a dyke she gave birth to Rachael's sister. The people including the new-born child were landed where Leverburgh now is, and left to fend for themselves. Rachael's mother built a shack near the shore to the west of this spot where she and her children remained as squatters for many years and made a life for themselves.

This story was told with a dispassionate matter-of-fact acceptance, and by the same token it is an extraordinary window into a different world. There is a pragmatic toughness in the face of adversity, a contempt for fate, a toleration of what would now be considered the unthinkable. And it happened probably in the 1850s or 60s, in a Scotland that has vanished. Rachael spoke no English: there can be few if any monoglot Gaelic speakers now. At that time in places such as Blairgowrie, it was not uncommon to hear country people who had come in from the Perthshire glens chatting in Gaelic. The kind of thatched house Rachael's mother built of stone and sods would begin to dwindle rapidly even in the 1920s. The *feannagan* or lazy beds on which they cultivated potatoes are now just heathery rickles of sandy peat, no longer nourished by creel-loads of seaweed from the shore. And the estate which had turned her and her people off their island is now but a phantom of the past, itself a victim of change. Anyone living in rural Scotland a century ago would have considered themselves to be living in times of great change, and it is worth while getting some idea of that Scotland, so that we can see where we have come from.

The Crofters Act of 1886 which was too late to protect Rachael's family had at least stabilised life in the North West, and would after a fashion fossilise it over the years. The sheep which had displaced people were themselves being pushed out by deer forest. Railways and steamer services were opening up ready access to the Lowlands for produce as well as people, and instead of the long trek through the hills, the stock would be loaded into trucks first at Inverness and Oban, and eventually at Lairg, Fort William and Mallaig. In the Lowlands, farmers looked back wistfully to the happy decades of "high farming" from the struggle of seemingly unending depression, their livelihood under siege from the ship-loads of cheap grain from the prairies of North America.

That same new world of the Americas and Australasia offered great possibilities, even dreams. Although the experience of emigration often turned out to be a very hard one – for instance the almost unimaginable shock of a first winter in Saskatchewan – there was no shortage of people willing to try. The Canadian Pacific Railway had brought off a deal with the government whereby it could settle people in the swathe of land through which the line cut, in order to generate the economic base that would help sustain it. The travelling agents of the CPR were regular lecturers to curious rural audiences, especially in the populous North East, where the vision of one's own *quarter* of ground was an attractive prospect to a small land-hungry tenant farmer or farm servant. Touching evidence of these emigrants regularly turns up in the Americas, South Africa and Australia and New Zealand in the form of fine smiddy-made ploughs stamped *Barrowman–Saline* or *Hally–Auchterarder* on the beam. It is said that these implements were often sent out to Scots pioneers bedded in timber crates filled with seed corn.

Empire was thus an economic reality that reached into the furthest parts of rural Scotland, and that had its effect. The country population which had been reluctant to provide soldiers to fight in the Crimea was changing its attitude to the idea of empire and the overtones of a different kind of patriotism that went with that. One relic of this change is the number of buildings which still carry the name *Drill Hall*. They were the bases of the Volunteer movement, where young men not only learned what were then considered the basics of soldiering, but competed keenly in contests of markmanship. In 1906 this matured into the formally constituted Territorial Army and Royal Naval Reserve, with an annual bounty providing an added incentive to the social interest, especially in the Crofting Counties, where it was a useful contribution towards the rent. As we shall see, this would have serious consequences for Scotland's rural population.

The framework of late Victorian rural Scotland was the estate. Then the estate was almost a kingdom within a kingdom, with the laird as sovereign and the factor as his unelected prime minister. Much hung on the character of the incumbent, but not altogether. Estates were private possessions with a public face, and with that could go a sense of obligation to the population at large. In part, this sense of social obligation was a reaction to new pressures. The time-honoured order of laird, tenant, servant and tradesman was being effectively questioned for the first time. Pressure came from newspapers with a wide circulation and an attentive readership. The "land question" embraced everything from a farmer's right to destroy the rabbits that decimated his crop to that ancient question – when Adam delved and Eve span, who was then the gentleman? Real parliamentary democracy was still a heady novelty, and as the Crofter and Irish MPs proved, it was something to be reckoned with. Some politicians had the imagination to embrace the spirit of the age, as did the 5th Earl of Rosebery. This eminent Liberal was also a keen Burnsian, and this may lie at the root of the systematic improvement of farm servant accommodation on his estates.

At the other end of the social spectrum were the descendants of what was known earlier in the last century as the peasantry. Now the word *peasant* has a pejorative edge to it, especially in Scots, where it denotes ignorance and bovine servility. Not so then. A peasant was, as the French root indicates, a country person. However, there is probably a simple reason for the drift away from the older usage, because at one time most peasants were understood to be small farmers, and in the Lowlands the Agricultural Revolution had turned many of them into farm servants and tradesmen, and the more prosperous ones into sometimes quite substantial tenant farmers. The old peasant character remained and remains mostly in the crofting communities, and to a lesser extent in those areas where there is still a higher proportion of small farmers, such as Orkney, Buchan or Lanarkshire. William Alexander's novel *Johnny Gibb of Gushetneuk* set in mid-nineteenth century Buchan gives a wonderful picture of a community that has as much in common with that old Europe of

Tchekov as with the Scotland of today.

That picture is not one of some simplistic rural idyll, but of a society which was still big and homogenous enough to have a wide range of internal character and variety. In any parish there would be several concentrations of population and activity. In the *big hoose* everything depended on an army of servants – people to carry the coals and stoke the fires, clean, wash, cook, and make the beds. When the laird walked out with his gun, it was over ground cleared of vermin by the keepers and under-keepers. When his lady drove out to visit, she was driven by a coachman behind horses groomed by stable lads.

This chain of service is something that had very much grown as the result of the earlier nineteenth-century prosperity. Far from engendering what is sometimes referred to as "feudal familiarity", it put more distance between different parts of society. If anything, this familiarity has returned with the collapse of the vast web of servitude that was the norm a century ago. This web was not confined to the gentry, professional people or the middling to bigger tenants. The prosperous tradesman's wife would have a lassie to break the sticks, redd the fire and scour the pans. In economic terms, it was one of the principal means by which wealth was recycled into the body of the population.

Most farms were small communities, and the bigger ones that predominated in Mid and East Lothian and the eastern Borders were like villages. They would contain upwards of four hinds or ploughmen, the shepherd and the cattleman, all with their often large families, besides the farmer, grieve, and the gangs of seasonal outworkers.

There would be at least one village – the kirkton – and usually several more. Many of these villages had their origins in the previous two centuries, deliberately planned by the lairds, while others were haphazard collections of little fues which the estates had encouraged. Generally they were the stronghold of the tradesmen and their adherents – the smiths who shod the horses, relaid the plough irons, mended the horse-drawn field machinery and shod the cart-wheels that the joiner made. That same *wricht* or joiner not only made the carts, but often a range of plain yet elegant furniture, and the flooring and roofing timbers and door fittings for the houses it would go in, and the coffins in which the inhabitants would be buried. Mill-wrighting was a development of the joiner's skill, essential to keep the wheels of the corn and threshing mills turning. In all the rural building trade was a big one. That required not only joiners, masons and slaters, but the rural industries such as quarrying, saw-milling and tile-making – including drainage tiles – and making and maintaining the roads that enabled the trades and farms to function.

The country tradesmen were the stable core of late Victorian rural society. Unlike the farm servants, who would often flit with their families to a different farm every twelve months, the tradesmen enjoyed the benefits of a settled existence. From their numbers would be recruited elders of the Kirk, and their children would attend the same school and enjoy continuity of education. Theirs was a life of modest but not overweening prosperity. Smiddy and joiner-work were but the most obvious trades. There were also fleshers, bakers, and tailors who would travel round the farms, and many other service trades. In the 1890s some villages still had the odd hand-loom weaver, a relic of a once numerous trade. When postcards became popular at the turn of the century, a common subject was a near-sighted and bearded patriarch representing the last weaver in the area peering through the heddles of his loom. There were numerous other callings which were not trades in the strict sense, but which were nevertheless real skills, such as dyking, draining, mole and rabbit catching. The villages might also contain the comfortable residences of the few professional people in the countryside – the minster in his manse with its glebe, and the doctor and vet, the latter

Lime kiln at Gorebridge, Midlothian, 1935. The burnt lime is being barrowed onto the truck. The brickwork shows how the old kiln had been refurbished, part of the drive, initiated by Walter Elliot as Minister of Agriculture, to move farming out of depression and neglect.

Dressing a mill-stone with a mill-pick in Midlothian, between the wars. Tradesmen such as the miller, joiner and smith were once vital to the rural economy.

two often in their pleasant villas at the edge of the villages.

Beyond lay the country town, the place of lawyers, accountants, seed-merchants, auctioneers, saddlers, coach-builders, the odd foundry, and not least the manufacturers and suppliers of agricultural machinery and equipment. The names of these old makers peppered the map of lowland small-town Scotland, and the common factor was the railway network. Coupled with an active farming press which could carry advertisements and an efficient banking system which could transfer credit, a national market was possible for these small firms. The commercial farming of the Lowlands and the more prosperous areas of the Highlands were part of the same scene, an industrialised Scotland, coping successfully with economic depression, conscious of and confident in her place as one of the principal economic dynamos of the Empire.

Thus we can see how at the beginning of our period, rural society, both Highland and Lowland, had a tremendous range and character. It was far from some simplistic picture of rich landowners, struggling tenants and the labouring poor. Poverty was there, and a constant menace, but the attitude to it was not always predictable. Worst of all was the prospect of old age. What happened when people were no longer able to work? If they had no savings, they had to keep working, or face the rigours of the poor law. If they were lucky, they might get the support of a charitable individual or organisation, of which the Royal Scottish Agricultural Benevolent Institution was one. Such bodies were not pious fancy, but met a very tangible and often desperate need, as many still do today. The introduction of old age pensions by the Liberal government in 1908 was a big step in the right direction, but it did not go far enough. People only became eligible by the age of seventy, which for many people then, after a lifetime of hard physical work, sometimes a deficient diet, poor housing and scant medical attention, was a decade and a half too late. Nevertheless, it was the beginning of the end for the *puirshoose*, that most dreadful invention of the previous century. Lloyd George's National Insurance provisions of 1911 tackled the problem of incapacity to work through illness, but in one quarter it provoked an unforeseen reaction. Robert Paterson was the farmer in Lendrum, by Turiff. He not only refused to pay the levy, but got the support of the local population, who reasoned that country people would be healthier than their urban counter-parts, and why should they subsidise the cost of the townsfolks' illness? When one of Paterson's beasts was poinded for payment, there was a riot, and the incident of *The Turra Coo* entered into the folk-lore of the North East. This show of independence was part of the old rural ethos, and the riot a sign that country society then had a rough and unruly streak that it is hard to imagine in the present climate of respectability.

That should remind us that the pre-war years were not in fact some halcyon age of stability, but ones of explosive industrial disputes and constitutional uproar – a tussle of will between the House of Commons and the Peers, the battle over Irish and also Scottish Home Rule, and related to that, proposals to extend the equivalent of crofting legislation to the Lowlands. Yet despite these upheavals, there was definitely the scent of happier times to come in the air. The fierce competition of food imports from overseas was reaching a balance, and there were signs of improvement. In 1899 the West of Scotland Agricultural College was founded, with the East and North colleges following in 1901 and 1904. These built on the tradition of sheer professional competence that had been an important ingredient in keeping Scottish farming afloat during the depression.

And as we know, so much was blown to the winds in the summer of 1914. The war had an immediate effect on the most remote parts of the countryside, because of the widespread involvement in the military reserves. The Territorial Army was not obliged to serve overseas, but that was no obstacle, because throughout Britain whole units simply volunteered, and that turned out to have a decisive effect on the course of events. The German army had swept down through neutral Belgium in a gigantic right hook, to be frustrated almost within gun-shot of Paris. In retreating north the Germans now also attempted to advance to the west in a race to secure the Channel ports which would supply any British army. The small British professional army stopped them at Ypres, but was decimated in the process. Many of those who stepped into the breach and solidified the line had been clipping sheep or bringing in the harvest somewhere in the Scottish countryside only a few weeks before.

Then came the general wave of recruitment. In the early phase of the war, it was reasonably assumed that it would be like the Franco-Prussian conflict of 1870, one of rapid movement and a single decisive campaign that would win or lose all. There was no thought of a drawn-out conflict in which the contestants would hack at the economic springs of their opponents. Recruitment in the countryside was brisk and unchecked, and the available statistics suggest that a third of Scotland's countrymen went to war, in effect half the men in the prime of life. Most survived, because for every man engaged in the fighting directly, there were several more to back him up, but it meant that the productive capacity of the countryside was seriously impaired.

To begin with this did not appear to matter, because by now Britain imported about three quarters of her food supply, and the seige by the Kaiser's submarines had not yet been attempted. Paradoxically, although the main focus of the war appeared to be on the Western Front, it was really won for the Allies on the sea and on the farms and in the factories. In the spring of 1916 the German fleet attempted to break out at Jutland. Although the Royal Navy sustained more casualties, the German fleet was so battered as to be useless for several months. With considerable misgivings, the Germans turned to unrestricted submarine warfare. Their near success in starving out Britain by destroying the sea-borne supplies revolutionised the conduct of the country's farming. The aim of conscription was not to supply more cannon-fodder, but to create a home front that would out-produce Germany. Farming not only became a reserved occupation, but drastic measures were taken to make good the previous damage to the labour force. One interesting memento of this can sometimes be seen in old photographs of the times. They show mere boys at the stilts of ploughs – proud of the fact that they are doing a man's job, released from school before their fourteenth birthdays by special dispensation. Other photos show groups in harvest fields, perhaps standing in front of reapers or binders. These include the old and the young and a majority of women, and often just one man in the prime of life – in uniform. He has been home on leave, providing the special occasion for the photo.

In a more general way, there was an unprecedented framework of regulations and targets administered by local and regional committees which directed the farming economy. For the first time wages and prices of produce were guaranteed to provide a stable framework for production. Corps such as the *Women's Land Army* were created. It worked. From a rotten harvest in 1916, there followed a massive sowing programme in the spring of 1917. Much ground that had been in grass since the 1870s was ploughed up. The upshot was a 20% increase in production, and in England, where there was more slack to take up, an astonishing 40%. That enabled Britain to survive until the U-boats were beaten. By way of contrast, Germany was racked by hunger into low morale and eventually internal collapse. The sad penalty was severe malnutrition, vulnerability to the epidemic of Spanish

Flu that swept Europe in 1918, and a dreadful increase in infant mortality. The latter created a resentment towards the British that figured as large as the supposed burden of reparations.

Peace brought just as great an upheaval to the countryside as war. Unwisely the government undid the framework it had created, and repealed the Corn Production Act in 1921. Farming not only plunged back into depression, but the value of land collapsed. For many old estates, it was the end of the road. There was often not just a burden of debt inherited from the previous depression, but death duties as the result of war-time casualties, sometimes repeated. There was a wave of tenants buying their farms, often at a low valuation. If they had been wise with their war-time income, many farmers were in a position to buy. It was the biggest upheaval in land tenure in Scotland since the great Abbeys had frittered away their assets at the time of the Reformation.

But whether for tenant or new owner-occupier or farm servant or crofter, the years to the nadir of 1930 were grim ones. In the Highlands the law now brought the promised land within reach. People could at last re-occupy the ground from which their parents and grandparents had been cleared, but for many depression made the prize worthless. Whole ship-loads of families sailed from the Western Isles for the New World. The names of the ships *Metagama* and *Minnetonka* signified a new life for those who sailed in them, but they also spelt out the heart-break of exile. And besides, the opportunities of emigration were dwindling. The New World was also hit by depression, and the gates welcoming those "yearning to be free" began to close.

Unemployment was not a serious problem in the Lowland countryside itself, as there was a trend of emigration to jobs in the towns. If anything, the population was static and ageing. One initiative born of the Great War revealed a great hidden need – for a more lively social life, especially for women. The *Scottish Women's Rural Institute* was an initiative of the Board of Agriculture to sustain war-time morale, started at Macmerry in East Lothian in 1917. The movement was an immediate success and spread rapidly to other parts of Scotland, and was copied in other parts of Britain.

One problem which would not go away until after Hitler's war was housing, and remained the main grouse of farm workers, more so than wages. Although lack of space might seem the worst thing to us now, in fact people had few possessions and were habitually adept at making the best use of what room they had. The worst problems were damp, lack of a good water supply and poor sanitation. Damp-proof courses in cottar houses were rare, and farm workers' housing was often sited with convenience to the road and steadings rather than on the naturally driest spot. A reliable stand-pipe at the gable-end was considered reasonable, and an internal supply a luxury! The reality was often a well that dried out in summer and a trek of fifty or a hundred yards and sometimes much further to get water. Sanitation was commonly non-existent or rudimentary, of the wooden privy and bucket variety. Flushing water closets were coming in, but only slowly. By the middle 1930s, only a quarter of the farm workers' housing had one. Although there were government grants towards effecting sanitary improvements, they were little taken up because by 1925 farming was in such a state that there was little money to make up the owner's contribution. The records of the times also hint at a sense of defeat in the face of such a big problem.

Various efforts were made to come to grips with the situation, including the formation of the various marketing boards to bring order into what was a hopelessly fragmented market for the producers. These would come into their own and serve their purpose, but the turning point in the fortunes of farming came in 1932, with the appointment of Walter Elliot

At Bankfoot Station, Perthshire, 1916, 3rd from the left is Mr Row, stationmaster. The railways played a vital part in the development of the countryside, encouraging the spread of horse-worked mechanisation from the 1860's. The Bankfoot Light Railway was one of the last country lines to be built, opened in 1906, and like many, it succumbed to bus competition in the post-WW1 years, closing to passenger traffic in 1932.

A binder and three-horse yolk at Dombmill, Aberdeenshire, during WW1. Most of the harvesters are women, old men or children as many of the men had gone to the war. The soldier in uniform is probably home on leave, and the occasion for the photograph.

as Minister of Agriculture. Elliot came of a family of well-known Lanarkshire auctioneers, and became a successful farmer at Bonchester Bridge in the Borders. What distinguished him from his fellow politicians of all parties (he was a Conservative) was a dislike of do-nothing excuses and a willingness to act. By a partial curb on imports he got Scottish livestock and English grain production moving again, and initiated longer-term schemes to retrieve the ground from the poor state into which it had fallen through years of neglect for want of liming and draining. The agricultural community today would be justified in looking back with a certain longing regret to the character of Walter Elliot, who had a broad and civilised outlook combined with intelligence and a champion's resolution.

One particular friend of Elliot's was John Boyd Orr, the first and brilliant director of the Rowett Research Institute at Aberdeen. Boyd Orr was mainly interested in nutrition, in both animals and people, and is the father of our modern interest in diet. When war again broke in 1939, Elliot and Boyd Orr had already played their part in preparing Britain for the trial that was to come. Farming was well on the road to recovery, and there was a scheme for food rationing worked out on scientific principles. Unpalatable though the latter sometimes was, it produced the healthiest generation that people could then remember, and for the urban poor, the first decent diet that they had ever had.

The lessons of the Great War were put to good use in Hitler's War from the outset. Although some country people were called up to the armed forces, this was not indiscriminate, and in cases such as the Lovat Scouts, highly appropriate, where stalkers and hill shepherds exercised their skills on the unfortunate Nazis. There was an invasion of the Scottish countryside of a peaceful and novel character. Most of the Poles who had escaped the Nazis and Soviets found themselves in Scotland in the autumn of 1940, and besides helping in rearing defences against invasion along the East Coast, they did much to help bring in the harvest in Fife and Central Scotland that year. Commandos trained in Lochaber, convoys carrying supplies to the Soviet Union assembled in the Western Sea Lochs, the Royal Navy prowled the northern oceans from Scapa and Invergordon, and the Royal air Force harried the Nazi submarines from what were then remote airfields such as Lossiemouth and Machrihanish.

Nothing exemplified the practical determination of these days more than the *Women's Land Army*. Town-bred girls found themselves lifting a collar over the head of a Clydesdale horse, forking sheaves, driving lend-lease tractors, felling forest trees and filling dung. It was a remarkable contrast to the dotty quasi-arcadian Nazi philosophy that reduced one half of humanity to glamorous breeding stock. It gave many women an experience of comradeship and the countryside that they would never have had otherwise. In contrast to these enthusiastic volunteers, for many Italian and German servicemen taken prisoner, the Scottish countryside became a merciful release into a civilised and kindly captivity, sufficiently so that, as with many Poles, a good number married locally and made it their home.

And what of those country people who worked the land through those years? In Lowland Scotland the six or twelve-month term, after which the farm worker might move to another fee, was still the general custom. The *Stand-Still Act* as it was popularly called, put an end to that. For the duration of hostilities, people could no longer move from one farm to another without good reason. Coupled with the weekly wage, this set a pattern that would long survive the war.

Although much has been made of the mechanisation stimulated by the demands of war, the farms of Britain and Northern Ireland were still largely worked by the horse. What changed was the formation of a basic network of dealerships, and a growth of mechanical know-how, greatly reinforced when an army that moved on trucks and jeeps and tanks came home. During the war tractors and combines were not widespread, but were apportioned according to productive capacity by the *Warags* or local Agricultural Executive Committees, or were used intelligently as a flying squad by the Government Tractor Service, which caught up with ploughing or harvesting on marginal land when it was falling behind. The result was not to mechanise the countryside, but make that possible.

The other ingredient was the technical development of tractor and combine. The first combine in Scotland was probably an *International* at Hedderwick Hill in East Lothian in the late 1920s, closely followed by the *Clayton* at the nearby Whittinghame Mains. The latter model, built at Lincoln from 1928, was the first European-built combine, and the only remaining example survives in the collection of the National Museums of Scotland, periodically exhibited at the Royal Highland Show. There had been tractors available since the invention of the internal combustion engine in the last century, but they were little more than expensive iron horses, working with adapted horse-drawn machinery. From 1933 Harry Ferguson, an Ulster Scot, developed the system that would mature into the "Wee Grey Fergie" produced by the Standard Motor Company after the war. Like many great inventions, the concept was simple – a three-point linkage between tractor and implement that made an integrated machine. This not only utilised the tractor's power fully for the first time, but by using hydraulics it enabled the drag of a plough to increase rather than diminish the machine's grip on the ground.

From 1946 the Ferguson system carried all before it. This would have been impossible but for the changed political attitude towards farming. The change of government attitude first wrought by Walter Elliot had at the outset of war matured into an understanding that if the country won through there would be no going back to the miseries of pre-war depression. The Annual Price Review established in 1948 was part of the radical changes made by Attlee's post-war Labour government. The Common Agricultural Policy has changed the emphasis, with a swing from the older Scottish tradition of mixed farming towards arable, but if anything it has continued this ethos, protecting the farming community against a radical swing to a totally deregulated market. Behind this lay the determination of the original Common Marketeers to prevent a wholesale invasion of mainland Europe's wrecked cities by a poverty-stricken population of ruined small farmers and unemployed farm workers.

Government support for farming certainly prevented a slide back into rural depression, and the brave new world of tractor and combine really took off in the 1950s. That decade saw a dramatic improvement in farm workers' housing, and thus the single biggest improvement in their conditions. There was a sustained effort to bring electricity to even remote parts of the countryside, thus extending the benefit of modern domestic conveniences to country people that many townsfolk had long taken for granted. As the old twelve-month term of work faded, a large part of the lowland country population became more settled than it had been for two centuries. In all this, the principal beneficiaries were women – hot running water to bath the bairns, no more flitting every year, and perhaps even the luxury of a washing machine.

Yet technological change forces its own kind of logic. As the horses disappeared, so did many of the old trades. No more horses for the smith to shoe, no more plough irons to be relaid. No more barn mills to be maintained, no more horse graith to be made and repaired. The old steadings that were designed round horse-working were no use for the new machines, grain-dryers, bulk-handling and storage, and the old milking byres were inefficient and did not meet the increasingly demanding regulations, so the traditional rural building trade which had grown up with the Agricultural Revolution gave way to contractors with the now familiar pre-fabricated portal-framed sheds. Some smiddies evolved into garages or agricultural engineering businesses. But generally, the whole trend was towards depopulation, most of all with the farm workers themselves. The horse which had replaced cattle in the plough barely two centuries before throughout much of Scotland was redundant. Swing ploughs and even fine match harness were dumped in old quarries, and many of the horsemen and more of their children sought a new livelihood in the towns. There was no great protest against this at the time, because it was accepted as part of that unstoppable tide, progress, and there were jobs to be had elsewhere. The penalty was closed schools, and other services such as the once familiar travelling shop. The buses had made many country railway lines unprofitable during the 1920s, but now it was their turn. The later spread of the car would not so much rival the bus, but become a necessity because the remaining services were so diminished.

Depression has never returned in the same virulent form that for the most part dominated the countryside between the 1870s and the mid-1930s, yet there have been rough patches, made worse by the more isolated nature of farming, and the victims often people who are good farmers but poor accountants. Although agriculture and the whole chain of food production is a vast and efficient industry, paradoxically farming people are not just a minority in the population as a whole, but in the rural population. Full industrialisation has finally caught up with agriculture, and only in the last ten years have people woken up to that fact.

NOTE: *Gavin Sprott is Keeper of the Department of Social and Technological History (which includes the Scottish Agricultural Museum) in the National Museums of Scotland.*

———◆———

"Farmers' wives made a lot of money with eggs. There was a deep litter and the hens were in all night and forenoon and then let out. This was the farmer's wife's income. She brought up the calves, milked the cows and did the hens. The kitchen floors were swept and scrubbed and they had what they call a clootie rug on the floor – this was done on a hook and lined at the back with a guano bag or corn bag. The stove was black-leaded. Mother was involved with the Red Cross during the war making socks and scarves and balaclava helmets".

———◆———

"The weather has definitely changed. We used to get seasons but the temperature changes even through the day now. May used to have warm and balmy nights with dampness and dewiness. We wore cotton frocks, bare feet and sandals and you could sit out in the evening (even where we were, near Dundee). Paths were hot under your bare feet."

SOUTH UIST IN THE 1930s

Margaret Fay Shaw

Margaret Fay Shaw lived in South Uist from 1929 to 1935, and thus observed and recorded with pen and camera a way of life barely unchanged for two hundred years. Communications to the Outer Isles were then still extremely basic, and although the lifestyle was hard and in some aspects primitive, the islanders lived with a dignity and community spirit that enabled them to surmount the harshness of their conditions.

South Uist is an island of sharp physical contrasts. It is twenty-two miles in length from south to north and some five miles in width. The west side is the flat *machair,* which is grassland that covers the mile-wide plain of sand that stretches along the shore of the Atlantic through all the Outer Hebrides. Here is the best crofting land, where most of the population of 2,700 live. It is excellent for grazing cattle and growing oats and bere, a four-rowed barley.

The east side of the island is wild and boggy moorland; crofter-fishermen live beside these lochs, as on the western plain, but the poorness of their land is compensated by the safe anchorage for boats and the access to the Minch for fishing.

My first months in South Uist were spent in the village of Lochboisdale, the port of the island. It had charm and friendliness, but there was not the opportunity for a beginner to speak Gaelic nor to hear the old traditional songs and observe crofting life. So on a sharp, cold January morning with the land white with frost I crossed Loch Boisdale in a sail-boat and walked the path to the cottage of Peigi and Màiri MacRae, where I was soon to make my home for the rest of my years in South Uist.

Glendale, the township where the MacRaes lived, was some two miles by path from a side road, and the easiest access to it was by sea. We usually journeyed to and from Lochboisdale in a sail-boat, the heavily built seventeen-foot type with a lug sail barked a red brown, which is the custom in the Hebrides. Such a pleasure on a fine day, it could be a terrifying experience on a black stormy night, tacking and threading between submerged rocks with a strong tide against a wind at gale force.

There were thirteen houses within the radius of a mile beside the sea loch and all had crofts of about five acres of peaty soil. Yet their potatoes produced an excellent crop, and enough oats were grown to feed their cattle through the winter. Each of the crofts had two cows with followers, and six of the crofts owned a few sheep. They were grazed on the hill which was their common land in the summer months and brought back to the shelter of the croft when the harvest was secure. The cattle were Highland or Highland-Shorthorn cross, which can stand the wet and stormy weather. The sheep were a small type of Blackface that is indigenous to the Hebrides, whose mutton is delicious and whose wool is handspun for blankets and tweed, the women not only knitting the socks and sweaters but heavy underwear for the men.

It was necessary for the men to have other work than crofting. Many were part-time fishermen. Lobster fishing was profitable if the lobsters reached London or Birmingham alive. Herring was precarious but could pay well and salt herring was a mainstay of the diet of the people. Others were deep-sea sailors on cargo or passenger ships sailing from British ports to all parts of the world.

The spring work of the croft began in February, when seaweed, used as fertilizer, was

Mary Anne, Katy and Sandy Currie planting potatoes with dibble and rake in North Glendale, Uist 1931. (Courtesy of Margaret Fay Shaw)

cut with a saw-toothed sickle called a *corran* on the tidal islands of the loch at low water of a spring tide. It was bound together in great bundles called *maoisean* and towed ashore at full tide so high that it could be left on the grass verge. The crofters then carried it in creels on their backs to the field, where it was left in a heap for a fortnight before being spread on the ground. There it was left until black and dry, the new grass showing above it, when the ground would be ready to turn. The fields were too small to use a horse-drawn plough, so the ground was dug with a spade or a footplough call a *cas-chrom*. This primitive-looking implement, whose name means crooked-foot, is of a type that has been used in various parts of the world since man first tilled the soil. The foot of the *cas-chrom* is made at an angle of 110 degrees to the long handle and the point is tipped with iron, which is pushed into the earth by the pressure of the man's foot on the wooden pin at the bend of the *cas*. It enters the ground at a slant, is tipped back and rolled to the side, where it deposits the clod. Though it does not reach the same depth as a spade, it cuts more evenly and without the back-breaking effort. The clods were then broken up with a heavy wooden rake of five thick teeth called a *ràcan,* and the field was harrowed by hand before the oats were sown.

The crofters planted their potatoes in 'lazy-beds' or *feannagan*. The plot was divided into long rectangles five feet wide and, with a rope as a measure, each rectangle was cut with a spade the length of the plot to the depth of five inches, this cutting along a rope line being known as *susadh*. A strip of seaweed three feet wide was spread down the centre of each bed. The crofter then turned a foot-wide clod or *ploc* to each side of the cut with a spade and laid it on the seaweed so that the strip was covered by a foot of earth on each side, with a gap or *taomoadh* of seaweed being left exposed. The two-foot-wide ditch or *claise* between the beds would be as deep as two feet to drain the ground, which was largely peat and often water-logged. The potatoes were then planted with a dibble or *pleadhag.*

Much of the work was done on a communal system: the lamb marking, the sheep clipping, when the men used to shear and the women fold the fleeces, and the dipping to control sheep scab, which was required in Uist by law four times a year. In June the peat was cut. The men would take each house in rotation for the days, usually not more than two, that each required for the year's fuel. Six men were needed to cut the MacRaes' peat, three men to cut it and three men to catch and lift the peat to the bank. On these days the women of the crofts would gather at the house of the one whose peat was being cut and help prepare a dinner for the men, of mutton or salt herring and potatoes. They would carry buckets of a drink called *deoch mhineradh,* which is cool, clear water with oatmeal stirred into it, out to the moor to refresh the workers. After the peat was cut it was left lying by the bank for a month, then three peats were stood on end with another on top. Later these were gathered to make small stacks until, at the end of the summer, when dry enough for burning, they were carried home to make the great stack by the house for the year's use. The peat in Glendale was of particularly good quality, being black and hard and burning long and well until reduced to a fine white ash.

In midsummer the hay and oats were cut with a sickle or a two-handled scythe and made into stooks in the field until the time when it was carried home to the shelter of the byre, where it was built into great stacks or *mulain,* the tops thatched with bracken and secured with ropes against the winter gales. The potatoes were dug in October and stored in the byre.

The women worked extremely hard. Though the men would return from the sea in early spring to cut the seaweed and turn the ground, the women carried the creels, helped with much of the planting, harvesting and carrying home the peats. They never complained of the scarcity of many things that the townsfolk are unable to do without. Nor in those black depression years did they ever voice the worry for their menfolk waiting interminably for a ship in a far-away city.

Most of the people lived in thatched houses which provide the ideal shelter, being warm and secure in the storms of a Hebridean winter and cool in the hot days of summer. It is not only that the thick walls of natural stone and thatched roofs fit into the landscape to the delight of the eye, but it is a design which has evolved through the centuries as being the best type of house for the Hebridean climate. The walls of the house are double, with a packing of earth or small stones between. They measure four feet thick, have rounded ends and are six feet high. The roof of wooden beams holds a layer of sods pinned together shingle fashion with wooden pins. The thatch of rushes or wheat straw is laid on top in such a way as to shed rain, and it is held down by ropes secured with stone weights, which reminded Dr. Samuel Johnson of curling pins. The low door opens into a narrow passage that leads both to the kitchen and to the *seòmbar* or best room, in which are two built-in beds, best furniture, lace curtains at the window, with treasured photographs and ornaments on the mantelpiece. Another small room, the length of the passage, opens off the kitchen and is called the *còsaid.* The walls are lined and papered, the floor of the room is of wood, the kitchen and passage of hard clay often sprinkled with white sand. The two chimneys at either end with open fires burn peat whose pungent aroma permeates everything in the house.

The MacRae cottage was on the slope of Easival and faced the north. To one who had been brought up in a wooded Pennsylvania valley and had never known a land without trees the contrast of Uist with nothing higher than the heather and the hay was to discover a new earth. The view from Peigi's door was of the life of the island: the small figures going about their crofts, the scholars crossing the hill to school, the solitary figure with a staff herding cows, the boat being dragged ashore, the brown sail on the loch, the smoke of the kelp fires on the sand dunes in the west; overhead the long approach of the flight of wild geese and swans. One watched the shore to see the state of the tide which governed the time of work on the sea. The direction of the wind was always noted, the shape of the clouds—as that strange cloud called *craobh* which stretched like a narrow blanket from north to south above the hills and gave the direction of the wind tomorrow. Winter nights brought an amazing vision of stars. Northern lights, called by the Gaels *Fit-chlisne,* men of the tricks, or the leaping, darting ones, appeared in long shafts of white, green and reddish light to form ribbon-like folds on the centre of the sky.

The sun in the winter months barely rose behind the hill and never shone on the cottage for weeks. But the hill gave protection from the south-westerly gales. The house had originally been a *taigh dubh* or black house, which is the oldest type of dwelling in the Hebrides and now rarely seen. Then the inside walls were not lined and the place for the fire was laid on the floor. The opening in the thatch for the smoke to escape was never directly over the fire in case of rain, but fire and door and chimney-vent were made according to rules that would draw the smoke out. But wind and rain will defy many better chimneys, and at times the smoke would gather in the rafters, and to avoid it one had to sit on a low stool. Peat smoke is not harsh and is said to be a disinfectant. The people have been accustomed to it since fires under cover began. The pleasant thing about such a fire was that there was room to gather round it in the true sense.

The light was then the crusie lamp or *crùisgein.* The fuel was fish liver oil, and the wick was made of the pith of rushes or *luachair,* which was dried by the fire and then plaited.

The MacRaes had rebuilt the house to the plan of the other thatched houses in

John Morrison using a cas-chrom or foot plough. South Uist 1931
(Courtesy Margaret Fay Shaw)

Glendale. The door was barely five feet high, particularly suitable for the little MacRaes, and it was painted bright blue. The kitchen was neat and gay, with a dresser filled with pretty dishes. All the furniture had been made on the island—the meal chest, the table, the long bench below the window, the low armchair and milking stools beside the fire. In the corner was the spinning wheel, with the basket of *rolagan* waiting to be spun. There were always a cat and kittens and a clever collie dog in the house. Every creature they possessed was a personality to the sisters. The sheep were given names and the roman-nosed ram with his great curling horns would call in the kitchen for his titbit. The cow was not only valuable property but one deserving constant care with true affection.

In the summer Peigi would have washed and dyed the fleeces. Then she would card the wool, combing, cleaning and making it into *rolagan* for spinning in winter. Peigi was continually singing as she spun. The rhythm of her foot on the treadle brought forth the songs as naturally as her fingers turned the wool to yarn. When there was sufficient for a length of tweed we took it in a sack across the hill to Peigi Iain Bharraich, the weaver, who lived with her sister in a house just big enough to hold themselves and the loom. When word came that it was ready it was collected and preparations were made for the great event of a *luadhadh,* or waulking, which is when the cloth is shrunk and made ready for the tailor. The planks that served as a bridge across the burn were made to serve as the table. A lantern hung from the rafters and shone down on the singers in their rough aprons, their heads tied in kerchiefs, their sleeves rolled high. The air was potent with the smell of hot urine, but no substitute will give the softness of texture nor set the colour, especially of indigo. When finished the tweed was thoroughly washed in a running stream and dried on the heather, exposed to the sun and wind for several days until perfectly clean.

From spring until autumn everyone was too occupied with work on the croft to spend time at the fireside. The long day-light of spring and summer (at midsummer it is twilight all night) make it possible to work outside until bed-time. But when the nights drew in and the harvest work was done, then began the *céilidh,* a word that means the gathering of friends to talk and sing and entertain each other. There were no radios and few newspapers but no lack of good company. There were many tales told of olden times. Witches were said to have the power of raising storms by knots that were tied in a piece of wool. Each knot meant a different strength of wind, and as each knot was loosened the wind increased. This piece of wool is called a *snàithlin,* and it had another use which is known to-day when it is made by one who has the power to remove the curse of the evil eye on cattle. A woman, whose mother's cow was so afflicted, told how her mother, finding nothing to cure the beast, walked a long way to the house of a man with this power. He named the one who had put the illness on the cow and he made a *snàithlin* for her with a certain prayer or incantation for the cure, but not in her sight. She was told to conceal it on the cow and that it would recover, which it did. I was always told that these incantations were made in the name of the Good One.

Tales were also told about supernatural animals such as sea cattle and water horses. An old man on the small island of Mingulay found a strange cow among his own herd one morning. She was a good milker, better than the others, so he kept every calf that came from her and did away with all his own. The cattle at that time were kept under the same roof along with the folk, and this night the old man was talking to his wife about the stray cow getting rather old, and they decided to kill it next day. In the morning when he let them loose the old cow made for the shore and all the rest followed her, to disappear into the sea. That night the old man was without a cow to his name.

The greatest chore for a wedding was the plucking and cooking of innumerable hens presented for the party by friends of the bride and bridegroom all over the island. A delegation was formed just to deal with this part of the feast, which consisted of cold chicken, roast mutton, scones and bannocks, fresh and salt butter, new cheese and many another special delicacy of the island, with the ever-present tea, and whisky and port wine for the toasts. Chickens were considered such an essential part of these feasts that when an epidemic killed a lot of hens on the island, Seonaidh Caimbeul, the local bard, made a song about it in which he refers to the grief of prospective brides at the impossibility of making proper wedding feasts without them.

Christmas Eve I walked with my Catholic friends to midnight mass at Dalibrog. It was a long five miles in the dark, and as we made our way west with a storm lantern around the slope of Carrisaval we could see far away many tiny lights scattered over the black *machair* moving north towards the church. Others joined us out of the darkness, and we made a long and cheerful procession. The Christmas story was read in Gaelic and they sang the Gaelic Christmas hymn, *Tàladh Chrìosta* or the Christ Child Lullaby. After church, shaking hands with each other and giving the wish of *Nollaig shunndach,* we walked the long road home in the early hours of the morning. There waiting was the feast of mutton, cooked the evening before, for it is the custom to kill a sheep for the first food on Christmas morning.

Rural Reminiscences
2. Some Prices in My Youth
(c. 1925–1935)

"I left school at 14 and came home to work for 2/6 a week plus keep. On the farm staff was a dairyman who also made the cheese at £1 plus his keep. There were 3 ploughmen and an odd man, 3 pairs of horses and a single one. I remember my uncle got into trouble from his neighbours because he gave the men a rise of 2/- a week. 34/- first man, 32/- second, 30/- for the third and £1 for the odd man. The wives of these men had to milk cows twice a day by hand, 7 days a week, they got 7/- a week for that. I am thinking of the middle twenties to the middle thirties. Prices of produce in those days: Oats £2 per ton. Milk 2d to 4d a gallon. Heifer to milk £14-18. Fat lamb 18/- to £1. Potatoes £1.0.10d per ton. Working horse was a big price at £30.

1921

150 acres of crops out of 1,000 acres total. (The usual rough guide was that one pair of horses was needed for every 80 acres of a farm).

Preston Farm, Duns, Berwickshire. (Courtesy of Robert Forrest Ltd)

) acres of crops out of the same 1,000 acres, still in the Forrest family.
e current workforce is two family, 2 full time and casual/part time when needed.

1991

Scottish representatives from the Women's Land Army at the Parade in London, 7th December 1945
(Courtesy of Mrs Fiona Murray)

THE WOMEN'S LAND ARMY IN TWO WORLD WARS

From information supplied by Mrs Doreen Butler

The WLA was originally formed during the First World War in an effort to increase home food production. Britain was still very dependent on imported food and at one point it was thought there was only three weeks' supply in the country. One ship torpedoed and sunk could have had serious consequences.

Recruits came from all walks of life and they were very brave women, not just to take on this rigorous and unaccustomed work but also because they had to face a great deal of ridicule and abuse. At the time the suffragette movement was fresh in everyone's minds and these early Land Girls in their "unladylike" breeches were mocked as they walked down the street. They were considered a disgrace to womanhood by male and female alike but they put a brave face on it and proved their worth for a wage of 2/- per week plus keep. They did the vital manual work which helped produce the food which was so desperately needed. Some even worked in forestry, felling trees with axes and saws, trimming branches and hauling the trunks by horse to the shore where the timber was floated before men took over to load it onto ships. Much of the timber was turned into pit props to keep the mines in production. Whilst those working on farms lived en famille or in hostels, the timber corps girls lived in barracks style camps and had a more military type of existence.

In the second war the wage started at 10/- a week which was raised to £1 after training. Uniform was provided unlike in the first War where the girls had to buy their own. Training consisted of a month on farm or at college where they learned byre work, piggery, poultry and field work as well as pest control including gassing, trapping and poisoning rats. They did this work willingly and cheerfully and made life-long friends in the process.

Once settled on the farm, in spite of having done a long day's work, many would help the farmer's wife wash dishes and do other household chores in the evenings. This wasn't part of their job but they felt they couldn't sit by and watch the missis working. After the war, some returned to their roots but many stayed in land related occupations or married farmers. Girls from the Land Army suffered war wounds – broken arms, legs, ribs, lost toes and feet – but they soldiered on and statistics showed afterwards that their efforts had raised farm output by 91%. Their country owed them a great debt but it was their own Benevolent Fund which helped them when they needed to get started in civilian life, government assistance was not available.

In May 1961 the RSABI took over the Scottish Women's Land Army Welfare and Benevolent Fund from the Scottish Office. The fund then totalled £7,548, and the Institution continued to award grants to former members of the service; or to women who had been associated with agriculture in Scotland over a period of years. The grants were not in the nature of annual payments, but were awarded to meet special circumstances such as illness or financial stringency.

The fund being so small, the Institution now awards the income annually to all those former Land Girls on their register – about 30.

Rural Reminiscences
3. Maybole, Ayrshire

"I was born and brought up on a farm. My brother and I attended the school in Maybole, a distance of 1¹/₂ miles night and morning in all weathers. My father and mother had a dairy farm, very primitive, and worked very hard to make ends meet. My father died when I was 13 and my brother 14. We left school and helped my mother carry on the farm – hand milking and the field work was done by horses. I had to help milk the cows and feed them, make hay and help with the harvest. We were very short of water having only a pump in the yard and all the water had to be pumped and carried in buckets. In the summer we had to cart water from Maybole to the farm with a water cart and horse – 1¹/₂ miles.

Some years were good if the weather was good for the hay and harvest but then the water dried up and gave us more work. Other years were bad when the hay lay in the fields for weeks rotting with the rain and of course the harvest was the same.

The work was all done with horses and early machinery with hand workers to tie the corn sheaves and gather the potatoes.

The farmhouse had no modern conveniences, no bathrooms, no toilet indoors, a wee hut up the garden. Paraffin lamps in the house and lanterns in the byres. Washing days was a wooden tub with a board to rub the clothes clean. Hot water from the boiler with a lit fire under it and the water all carried from the pump.

Having little water, our milk was all cooled in milk boynes on the floor in the dairy and then had to be filled into the churns to be lifted by a lorry to go to the creamery. We made butter with a churn which had to be turned over and over. Often that was my job which I didn't like but I had to do it.

I married in 1941 to a farmer and had to endure the war years with very little to carry on with. We had to grow a lot of cereal and if the weather was bad it was very hard work and a big loss. We worked with Land Girls and German prisoners who were good workers.

It was all very hard work but if I had to I would do it all over again."

(now aged 78)

'Alexis', a German prisoner of war carting potatoes at Devon, Kennoway, Fife, 1949. He would soon be repatriated. Here he still has his German army jack-boots.

LIFE ON TWO FARMS

R.S. Hunter

"In the event of war a Women's Land Army will be organised" – so said the National Service booklet issued to every household early in 1939.

Recruitment must have been brisk as my application to join was accepted on an impressive document dated 19th September and my number was 1223. The lady from the "War Ag." who interviewed me asked with a doubtful glance at my small size, "Do you think you will be fit for the heavy work involved?" I replied that I was quite strong and was used to being out in all weathers. I was ordered to report for a month's training at Auchincruive.

A motley collection of girls descended on and overflowed the hostel and farm where the staff struggled valiantly to give us what would now be called "work experience" but there were just too many of us for it to be satisfactory. We were divided into four groups, spending a week in each of four sections: Dairying (machine and hand milking, feeding calves, mucking out etc), Pigs (pandemonium), Bullocks (not memorable) and Fieldwork, including tractor-driving which was much too memorable on one occasion when a tractor, driven by a learner, went out of control on a hill and "couped" just missing the girl who rolled clear while the rest of us watched, horrified and powerless to help. A journalist arrived that afternoon to give us a write-up but she missed a scoop as everyone had the sense to keep mum!

There were lighter moments – one recruit actually fell for an old gag and was sent to the farm-manager's office for 'a left-handed hammer' where she was told solemnly "I think this one will do."

The month certainly showed us what we were in for in the way of early rising, back-breaking work in all weathers – and smells! – and some gave up. Some, too, could not afford to wait till a job became available as we were not yet needed on farms.

However, in a month or two my friend Alex and I were lucky enough to be applied for and went to work on a marginal farm of about 300 acres, plus hill land, near Ballinluig where we lived in the farmhouse with the Boss and his wife 'as family'.

Our uniform, for which we gave up a number of clothing coupons, awaited us and it was quite a thrill to be kitted out and feel that we were really part of the Defence of the Realm. We wore khaki drill dungarees and long jackets and gumboots mostly for work, with cream-coloured aertex shirts and a green pullover. There were also fawn corduroy breeches of indeterminate shape, knee length woollen stockings and strong brown shoes, a W.L.A. tie and an armband. Later a raincoat, leather boots and canvas leggings and a warm overcoat were added. And of course there was the hat, tortured into many shapes by the more inventive Land Girls!

The farm stock consisted of out-wintered spring-calving Galloways, cross Highland and blue-grey polled cattle, a large white boar with a few sows and the consequent litters of piglets, an Irish gyp called Paddy (what else?), a mare with yearling colt, some farmyard hens and turkeys and a fluctuating number of cats. There was also a dear old deaf collie dog.

A large part of the land was steep and not suited for the war-time compulsory growing of cereals. It was also back-lying and exceedingly cold in that hard winter of 1939/40.

We were initiated into all the jobs about the place and gradually found the rhythm that was most effective and consequently least effort. We did the mucking out, milked the house-cow, fed the pigs, learned how to harness and yoke Paddy and load and cart straw

Mrs Jean Gray, who served in Ayrshire during the Second World War.

Mrs Annie Young, who served as a Land Girl in both World Wars.

Land Girls 1914-18 War.
In the centre is Christine Manson.
(Photographs courtesy of Mrs Doreen Butler)

and turnips for the beasts, avoiding collisions with gate-posts en route. There were a few minor inconveniences – for instance the saddle brackets were fixed at a height suitable for the average man and we were in danger of being floored, literally, when lifting a heavy cart saddle up at arm's length!

We were well fed but always ravenously hungry and not above sharing the pigs' potatoes which we cooked in an outside boiler.

When there was enough milk we made butter in a hand held glass churn. This was an evening occupation when the four of us were sitting round the fire. We would pass the churn from one to another till the butter came and the Missus then washed it and shaped it into pats with the wooden 'scotch hands'.

The summer of 1940 was lovely. Haymaking was another new experience, making the acquaintance of the horse-rake and tumblin' Tam and learning to turn the swathe with hayforks, another rhythmic job. The hay was made into small ricks to be carried up to the hay-loft later. While working down by the river a "dook" at tea time gave us energy to carry on into the long, light evenings.

After a few weeks pause, catching up with other chores like weeding potatoes or turnips, harvest was upon us. We learned to scythe roads to let the binder into the field, gathering and tying sheaves out of the swathes. Then it was a case of trying to keep up with the binder as we stooked madly behind it, almost hoping for a break-down! After 'three Sundays in the field' (in a good year) the corn was ready to be carted and the task of building loads that would stay on the trailer was learned the hard way! Hard, too, for the stack-builder who got many a sheaf landing on the back of his neck instead of conveniently to his hand. Here I must pay tribute to the patience and forbearance of the regular farm workers towards us amateurs.

Then came tattie picking, then turnips to shaw and pit for winter feed – and so the first year ended.

On completion of each six month's service we were awarded a cloth half-diamond to sew on our armbands and after two years our County Representative kindly arranged a party for us in Perth where we were presented with new red armbands and partook of a substantial tea. (Dried-egg cakes and marge-spread sandwiches of course, but filling). We enjoyed meeting girls from the rest of the county, including two from our training month. We swapped yarns and experiences – "We do so-and-so," and "My Boss says he'll give me a shot at ploughing". We all felt we 'belonged' by this time.

After two and a half years we felt it was time to move on when we could do so without leaving our employers in the lurch. Again we were lucky, getting jobs on a big dairy farm working closely with the Glasgow College in new treatments for mastitis, and in crop experiments. I worked a wise and powerful Percheron mare most of the time, carting kale, hay, silage and straw for the dairy herd; while Alex worked in the poultry unit and the dairy. As I could drive a car, enjoyable interludes were trips to the smiddy with parts of machinery to be welded.

Sometimes I drove a tractor. One of these was a Fordson with flanged metal front wheels which made steering tricky as the wheel tended to take charge and whirl round. No-one warned me of this the first time I tried it and I nearly ran into the binder I was supposed to be towing! The men were very nice to us but they were a little inclined to stand and guffaw at our efforts before showing us how to do a particular job!

Naturally work was more compartmentalised on this 600 acre farm and there were no extras in the way of milk, eggs and butter, as milk (in ten gallon churns) went to the Milk

Marketing Board Creamery and eggs to the packing station. How the farm manager's wife managed to feed us on the rations, or the money – our pay was 28/- a week with 14/- taken off for board – I can't imagine.

One unexpected 'perk' was silage treacle, strong but sweet, of which we could take home a small tin to our grateful parents. The big treacle barrel was kept in the stable while we were silage making and that led to my discomfiture one weekend. We must have been working overtime on a Saturday and, as I was going to the theatre in Glasgow (a rare treat), I was in a hurry to catch the bus. The foreman and I were on our way in with the horses when he offered to 'sort' my mare so that I could get away promptly. That was fine and it was a good show, but it was my turn for stables on Sunday morning. When I got there, sleepy-eyed, it was to find my mare with a slightly bemused expression and treacle dripping from her whiskers, standing in a pool of treacle which had flowed from the barrel. Somehow she had got loose and nuzzled the bung till it came out. Of course I couldn't say the foreman had tied her up! The farm manager remarked sourly "I thought you prided yourself on being able to tie knots!" I had to spend most of Sunday morning shovelling and sweeping treacle for the next day's silage (fortunately it wasn't wasted) and scrubbing the stable floor. That the mare was none the worse was some consolation.

We made hay on this farm by the quick and efficient Proctor system (tripods and vents) and it was ready in a week or so for baling out of the ricks which were brought to the baler by tractor sweep. You had to be pretty nippy taking off the rope and removing the wires and tripods without getting in the way of the men forking to the baler.

Turnip thinning was usually done by an itinerant gang on piece-work, but I remember vividly one occasion when there was a smallpox scare and all the farm staff had just been vaccinated. The foreman, two tractor drivers and three or four land girls (there were now six of us) made up a turnip thinning squad – an awkward one right enough as we were suffering from sore and swollen arms and armpits and hoeing was not the best occupation for us. The farm manager had said, tongue in cheek, "It doesn't matter so much if one of you gets smallpox, but if you do, all the milk will have to go down the drain!"

Small amounts of beans, rye and barley were grown as experiments for the College but much the greater part of the cereal crop was oats. Combine harvesters were almost unknown – I remember cycling quite a distance just to see one of these monsters working!

A squad of Italian prisoners came to help at harvest, decent men who were only too glad to be out of the fighting. They said "No Mussolini, no war."

The corn was stacked beside the nearest farm road where the travelling threshing machine, powered by an enormous engine called a Foden could park conveniently alongside. Two land girls were always given the job of cutting the bands as they passed the sheaves to the man feeding the drum. Usually one of us was put on the dusty job of bagging the chaff. The excuse, reason really, was that corn sacks weighing $1^1/2$ cwt were beyond our powers, though we carried 1cwt bags of tatties and bales of hay on our backs regularly.

We grew quite a large acreage of potatoes. The Ministry of Food kept telling us, via a cartoon character called Potato Pete, that potatoes were "Good for us and gave us energy" (carrots helped us to see in the dark).

Throughout the country, school children were given 'potato holidays' to help with the lifting. One year Polish soldiers came from a nearby camp, but whether they regarded the outing as a holiday or a fatigue is questionable!

Life wasn't all toil – there were Saturday night 'hops' in the village and an excellent branch of the Young Farmers' Club with farm bookkeeping, lectures on stock rearing etc and debates on the syllabus. There was a first-aid class run by the farm manager, which was attended by a lot of retired people where land girls were 'Volunteered' as casualties. This had its excitements as we were lowered from windows or carried on stretchers in the blackout.

Three years come and gone – the war over at last! No more bombs or blackout, no more attacks on Atlantic convoys bringing food desperately needed in addition to the vast amount now grown on British farms. News came, some happy, some sad, of far-scattered relatives and friends. Decisions had to be made about our own futures.

Although the W.L.A. was not disbanded till, I think, 1952, one advantage of not being classed with the Services was that we could resign when it suited us to start training for our chosen career, greatly assisted, as we got no government gratuity, by the W.L.A. Benevolent Fund which gave generous grants.

Meanwhile the farming year revolved as always, and we got on with the job – "the land must be served".

I intended to leave at the end of 1945 to take a course in shorthand and typing, subsequently applying for a post as farm secretary, but on 7th December my career as a land girl reached its peak. Scottish girls who had served throughout the War were invited to London to join in a march to Guildhall and a party at the Mansion House where Her Majesty the Queen, our Patron, would address us and present us with 6-year armbands.

It was a happy occasion, as informal as possible, and Her Majesty's speech made us feel proud to belong to the W.L.A. One phrase especially expressed what we had often felt: "The Land Army has been fortunate that even during the darkest days of the War, its task has been one of creation, not destruction."

Bringing home the peat in the Tong district of Lewis

Rural Reminiscences
4. Early Days in Papa Westray

"I was brought up on a small farm. I loved the animals and although I am now retired my nephew puts animals on the farm and I look after them to count them and see that they are alright. That's during the summer when the beasts are on the grass.

School days were different from today: a coal fire in the room, walking to school and sometimes getting soaked, children nowadays are collected by car, they miss a lot of the beauty of walking along the beach or along the road.

Work on the farm was hard but lightsome and folk were contented those days – not much money to spare but plenty work for everyone. Nowadays with modern ways of farming there's not many workers required and that's one thing that causes unemployment.

Food mostly all came from the farm, not much bought at the shop, plenty milk, butter, cheese, bere meal, oat meal, potatoes and turnips.

Wartime the navy took over the North Hill for a practice shooting range, various houses had to keep the lads who were in dug-outs on the hill to guide the shells from the warships. On one occasion a shell landed quite near our house and a neighbour's beast was killed. We kept eight of the lads, two at a time, and one of them still writes to me at Christmas and that's over fifty years ago.

The farm was worked with horses until after World War 2. In 1950 I bought my first tractor, the tractor that I still use is 31 years old. First we had a one horse reaper for cutting the hay and crop and then we had a reaper with a bigger cut pulled by two horses. Sheaves and all lifted by hand and bound and stooked. When the tractor came we had a binder – what an improvement, sheaves ready to stook!

We had good years and bad, sometimes late before the harvest was finished. A great miss nowadays with no stooks on the land all goes into silage. Hay cutting was done by the reaper pulled by horses then turned by hand and when dry it was made into coles and then carted into the yard and built into stacks.

When the tractor came the hay was turned by a hay turner and when dry was baled and built into stacks.

There was no modern conveniences – no water on tap, water was carried with buckets for our use and to the animals when inside during the winter."

"Rankin the Domini, weel he wisnae a richt domini by the way. Mrs Rankin, she was a townsbody."

"We had a small engine and we had to get petrol. We needed coupons of course and we'd carry this 2 gallons of petrol six miles up the road. Some folk got the baker to bring it in his van. Tins of petrol sitting in the front of the van and charged up accumulators like car batteries but quite small for the wireless. The baker had parrafin and everything."

A Ferguson TE20 - the Wee Grey Fergie - and a Claas Super combine harvester in Fife, 1950's. It was this combination of a tractor with hydraulics and a three-point linkage, and the combine, that drove out the horse and finalised the industrialisation of farming.

A ploughing match in Arran. What the photo omits is the mass of spectators. The competing teams have stopped for the photo. There were prizes not just for the best ploughing but the best turned out pair o horse, and the most handsome ploughman!

Rural Reminiscences
5. Prince

I have many memories of working with horses on the farm but the horse which I remember best was called Prince.

Until I moved into sheltered housing in Grantown on Spey two years ago I had lived all of my 74 years at a farm on Dava Moor which had been farmed previously by my father and grandfather. In their day, horses were the mainstay of the farm. Each Clydesdale was bred on the farm by my forebears. Heugo Footprint was the best stallion that ever served in the North East of Scotland – Prince and Bess were two of his off-spring! Breeding the horses created a lot of work as each horse had to be broken in and trained for its job.

Prince was a gelding and a very temperamental horse. He was a real live wire! He would bite and kick and he was not to be trusted. Often while standing in his stall he would paw the ground so hard that sparks flew from his shoes. However he was kept because he was a horse of unbelievable strength. There was a whole birch tree which we cut down and he pulled it all by himself. We put a "tie-him-back" on to his nose to keep him beside the mare, Bess, while they were working as a pair, so that he did not pull in front. The tie-him-back was a loop to which a rope was attached.

When I was in my teens an incident happened which is imprinted on my mind. My father was aged about 76. (He was married when he was 60 and people said he would never see his son – me – "haud the ploo" but he did, he died when he was 86). He had been with one of the horsemen to the loch to gather rushes to take home to feck (thatch) the corn stacks. My father was sitting on the front of the cart, pulled by Prince, getting a carry home. They were coming through the edge of the wood. Prince, as ever, was in front of Bess, the mare. Prince always had to be in front! The cart went over a tree stump and the cart, the contents, the horse and my father all went overboard! My father landed below Prince with his arm wedged underneath the horse. I heard Willie, the Horseman, who had been leading Prince, calling for help and ran to see what had happened. By this time Willie was sitting on the horse's head to keep it from rolling on top of my father. The horse was on its back with four legs in the air!

I knew I must get help very quickly. There was no one else at home and we had no telephone so I ran 2½ miles to the nearest farm to get help. Danny and Lachie came racing back with me. We used a fallen birch tree and gradually levered up the horse sufficiently to let my father out. He had been jammed under the horse for more than 2 hours, conscious all the time. We lifted him onto the back of Bess's cart to get him home. His spirits were amazing for he remarked "I am like a partridge with a broken wing!" We called the doctor and firstly he was taken to Grantown and then to the Royal Northern Infirmary in Inverness.

The doctor gave him a choice. The choice was to have his arm amputated or to have it as a useless rigid limb?! The arm was very badly broken and squashed due to the horse wriggling and moving all the time. My father decided to keep his arm and for the rest of his life he suffered considerable pain with it.

Prince remained a work-mate of mine for many years after, when I worked the farm. I said a very sad "Good-bye" to him and Bess in the early 50s when I decided to replace them with a tractor!

A CENTURY OF WORK IN SCOTTISH FORESTS

John Fowler

Two old photographs show the death of a forest giant. In the first, an elderly forester sits wedged between two buttress roots at the base of the trunk, his watch chain dangling over an ample waistcoat, his face framed in snow-white beard and whiskers, hands resting imperiously on his knees. The second picture shows the aftermath. Seven shirt-sleeved men bend over a saw as it bites into the thick trunk. Behind them, a heavy horse is being hastily led away from where the tree will fall.

This event is recorded in the journal of the Royal Scottish Arboricultural Society (now the Royal Scottish Forestry Society) for 1924. The season is spring, the scene Drummond Hill overlooking Loch Tay, and the tree a larch said to have been planted by an Earl of Breadalbane around 1770. After more than 150 years of vigorous growth the timber was judged sound. It was, declared the writer, "the outstanding stem of many larch trees of huge dimensions on Drummond Hill"; and while regretting its passing he took consolation in the fact that the newly established Forestry Commission, to which the estate now belonged, had already replanted 600 acres of hillside.

The workers pictured – not a Forestry Commission squad but men from contractors identified as "Messrs M'Ainsh of Perth" – were using traditional forestry methods which would continue to be the rule, by and large, for another forty years. Brawn and (literally) horsepower provided the motive force. The satisfying thud of the axe, the rhythmic rasping of the hand-held saw and the jangling of bridle and chains were all familiar woodland sounds. So were the voices of men, lots of men – for forestry had always been a highly labour-intensive trade. When Lord Lovat, an eager proponent of pre-First World War reforestation (who subsequently became the first chairman of the Forestry Commission) helped to draw up a specimen plan for forestry development in the Great Glen he envisaged a huge increase in employment. In the Fort Augustus area alone it was calculated that new plantations would require from the start an additional labour force of more than 60 men and that as the first crop of timber reached maturity and had to be felled the number would rise significantly.

The breakdown of the original 60 makes interesting reading: one head forester, three assistants, seven men to patrol the plantations, kill vermin and tackle any fires, three trappers to kill rabbits, thirty planters with six boys to help them, ten woodcutters, three foremen fencers, plus extra part-time labour for the tree nursery.

Afforestation, it was believed, would stem the drift from the countryside and help to repopulate the Highlands. It was calculated that whereas a thousand acres of rough hill grazing would support only one shepherd, the same ground converted to plantation would require 10 woodmen to look after it. Later on there would be proof. In Argyll it was noted that forest employment had increased tenfold over 30 years, from 95 in 1930 to more than 900 in 1960.

There are veteran forest workers who well remember the old style of working. Alastair McLean, who still lives in Cowal where he worked for 42 years, joined the Forestry Commission on leaving school in 1937 at the age of 14. His weekly wage was twelve shillings and sixpence. At that time the conifer forests which now girdle the lochs and lower slopes were being planted. Alastair was a "nipper", one of the lads who kept the planters supplied with seedlings brought up to the site in horse pack saddles. As an adult he tackled all the forest jobs. Using a big-handled spade called a cutter he dug drains in the wet, heavy soil in preparation for planting. He cut down bracken with a heuk (sickle) and

(Courtesy of Forest Life Picture Library)

*A Locomo 990 grapple-head harvester felling a Sitka Spruce, April 1989, Nithsdale, South Scotland
(Courtesy of Forest Life Picture Library)*

cleared the slopes of birch, willow and oak scrub. He planted the young trees in upturned mounds, thinned them when the time came and finally felled the mature trees with axe and crosscut saw. He worked in all weathers, donning oilskins when it rained. And in summer when the midges attacked (forests are midge-friendly environments) he rubbed himself down with a mixture of olive oil and the Forestry Commission issue of Citronella.

At one stage Alastair and his pal Jock, who worked as a team, bought a pair of horses from a local farmer and were employed by the Commission to extract timber – work which earned them an extra £5 a week to help with the horses' keep. He remembers the big white fivers in his pay – for some reason the Forestry Commission paid in Bank of England notes.

Alastair's father was also a forestry worker and in line with the Forestry Commission's policy on land settlement, a few acres of croft came with their cottage pre-war. They kept a cow and pig, grew vegetables and cut the hay. Every year a calf was walked eleven miles to market at Strachur, and every Christmas the pig was slaughtered and the pork and bacon salted down.

The Forestry Commission had always housed its workers and latterly a network of forest villages were built, sometimes as new communities in isolated settings, or as appendages to existing villages. These houses were made of timber, and the typical design was not Scottish but Scandinavian. The forest villages are easily identified today, though few of the present occupants are likely to work at forestry. The experiment seems never to have been completely successful, and after a brief flourishing in the 1960s forest villages became redundant as transport and improved roads made travel easier and mechanisation reduced the need for labour.

Even before the Great War of 1914-18 there was a strong lobby to replant hill and moorland with trees. It was reckoned that less than five per cent of Scotland was wooded, a total that included estate plantations, scattered relics of ancient woodland, patches of scrub, farm shelter belts and the pleasure groves of policies and parks. The great surge of tree planting by progressive landowners during the past 200 years had died out – with one or two exceptions – by the middle years of the nineteenth century, and the parlous state of British forestry in comparison with other European nations was frequently bemoaned. The drive was spearheaded from Scotland, where barren Highland glens and hillsides were seen as the ideal territory for reforesting. Curiously, even the great landowners who led the movement – no socialists they – often seemed happy to campaign for a state forestry service.

It was the shock of war and Britain's dependence on imported timber which spurred on the creation of the Forestry Commission in 1919 (the French forests of the Vosges and the Jura having supplied most of the British Army's needs at the front). Timber was a vital commodity required for essentials such as pit props and railway sleepers. But almost as soon as the Commission was set up it nearly floundered, threatened by the notorious "Geddes axe" and the call for savage cuts in public spending during a post-war financial crisis. It was saved by dint of desperate lobbying, but only just.

In surviving it changed the face of Scotland, though this was not achieved without criticism. There was vocal opposition even in the early days to its policy of blanket and widespread planting of conifers, apparently with little concern for the way it altered the landscape and often with too little care for what species were best suited to the ground. Without doubt, large tracts of young spruce trees (which more and more became the favoured species), all of an age, thickly planted in precise rows and in starkly geometrical blocks, were and remain an eyesore. These plantations, it's true, improved somewhat with age, whereupon on reaching maturity they were customarily clear-felled, leaving the ground, for a time at least, a sorry mess of stumps, tangled brushwood and tainted with the drab colours of decay. Not that the forestry Commission has been the sole culprit. Indeed the worst environmental sins of recent years have been the creation of private plantations in quite inappropriate situations merely to provide tax breaks for investors; this led, for example, to irreversible damage to the unique wet moorlands system in the flow country of Caithness. Fortunately the tax system has been reformed to stop this scandal.

Even at the turn of this century some mechanical aids to forestry existed, though on a limited scale. A writer in 1901 promoted the use of a ten or twelve horsepower steam engine with high pressure boiler to be fuelled by waste from the estate sawmill. He also advocated the use of traction engines for sawing and hauling timber from the woods, though he accepted that on rough ground horses were preferable, since "wages and the upkeep of the traction engine would under ordinary circumstances be greater". The writer envisaged that "the principle of the motor car may in time be an improvement on the traction engine".

A flood of technological change has transformed forestry practice in the past 30 years. At the start of the 1960s horses were still widely used for dragging timber from the forest. By the end of that decade they had been superseded by the winch, just as chain saws had made the axe and the crosscut saw obsolescent. Interestingly, there has been a modest renewal of interest in horse dragging recently, with a growing opinion that a horse can still prove economical on difficult terrain, and – an important factor when protection of the environment is important – treads much more gently on the ground than the compacting force of heavy machinery. Not long ago I watched logs destined for a new roof at Stirling Castle being extracted from an oakwood near Tyndrum. For Peter Matyjasek, the contractor, this marked a return to well-tried ways – he worked horses when he started in forestry more than 30 years ago.

Chain saws in their turn have been followed – though not superseded – by sophisticated machinery. The Forestry Commission introduced its first harvester, a multi-purpose, hi-tech machine which can handle 500 tons of timber in a week, in the 1980s. Now harvesters are widely used wherever large-scale felling takes place. Such a vehicle takes only a few minutes to transform a sturdy growing tree into a pile of logs ready for transporting. The harvester rolls up to a tree, grips the stem, saws through the trunk, upends it and strips off the branches, slices the tree into given lengths and then deposits the sawn and trimmed logs in a neat stack. The men who operate these machanized systems are the new kings of the forest, highly skilled technicians far removed from the forest workers of yesterday, as reflected in their earnings of £500 or £600 a week. Unskilled forest workers will probably get about half that in their pay packets.

Reflecting on such changes, Roger Hay, chairman of the Forestry Contracting Association, points out that in the early post-war days men had to be recruited from the labour exchanges, perhaps 200 at a time, to make up the mass gangs required for extensive planting or road making. After the 1960s the labour force dwindled as mechanization took over and the emphasis rapidly switched from muscle power to skills. Now one man in a cab performs the work of a whole gang, in less time.

The forester of today is likely to be a self-employed freelance rather than an employee, working in a small squad – and sometimes alone – formed through the grapevine of personal contact. "You may go to an experienced man whose work you know and trust and he will then recruit his own picked squad", says Colin Blyth, who is district manager at Stirling for Tilhill Economic Forestry, one of a number of forest management companies which have grown up since the war. In his district, which stretches from the Pentlands in the south to Pitlochry in the north, he is responsible for 9000 hectares of woodland. Regular seasonal work such as tree planting, fertilizing, heather control, and routine maintenance – the silvicultural side of forestry – is carried out by a workforce of three directly employed men and another fifteen or twenty under contract. The harvesting operations of thinning and felling are carried out by specialist contractors. Blyth says that the average forest worker of today is more knowledgeable and adaptable than his predecessor. Often left to his own devices, he (sometimes she) has to use his initiative in ways that were not expected of the old gangs: for example, in an area to be planted mainly with birch he will be expected to recognise where a different species – say, alder in the wetter patches – will grow better.

One reason for the appearance of forestry management companies is the post-war shedding of estate staff and the consequent need to hire specialists to look after private woodlands. At the same time private planting – for commercial, community and amenity woodland – has been encouraged by tax concessions and substantial government grants. Lottery money available for Millennium Forest native woodland projects has provided another boost. The coming century is likely to see a dramatic change in Scotland's forest cover, both in extent and in its nature – as great a transformation, perhaps, as the past hundred years has brought.

John Fowler is a writer and freelance journalist with a particular interest in environmental matters.

———

"Naebody has lanterns nowadays. They did need cleaning because they got full of black reek and ye didna see. There was the Alladin with long thin glass going away up and brass lamps and the Tilly lamp. The Tilly lamp gave you an instant light for your fag. The byre lanterns were square and there was a wee lampie for the bedroom. Lamps a' ower the place. The glasses used to break. You had to clean the lamps every day. The best way was to wash them, then dry and polish."

———

"My mother's brother cut snow for weeks. 1947 was a cracker of a winter, we were blockit in."

THE WOMEN'S TIMBER CORPS

One forgotten branch in which 1,000 women served in Scotland during the Second World War was the Women's Timber Corps. In England and Wales the numbers reached 3,900, and throughout Britain the total would probably have risen even higher but in July 1943 further recruitment was stopped, as it was to the Land Army, to force women into other less popular types of war work. From the start the Women's Timber Corps acquired an up-market image which the Land Army would never achieve and which land girls resented. One middle-class girl, volunteering for the Land Army, was told by her recruiting officer, 'You're much too well educated to be a land girl. Why don't you join the Women's Timber Corps instead?' What they see as totally unwarranted snootiness on the part of the sister force rankles with many old land girls to this day. 'They always thought they were the élite,' said one girl. 'I wouldn't like to have done some of the jobs they did – like working in the sawmills. But they weren't expected to master the sheer variety of skills that a land girl in general farming had to take on.'

Training varied according to what the girls would be doing once they started work. The chief task of the Women's Timber Corps girls who worked in Scotland, whose vertiginous pine-clad hills proved a valuable source of much-needed softwood, was felling trees for pit props. Their training, therefore, concentrated on general forestry, though the girls could, if they wanted, learn sawmill work and haulage using tractors and horses. In England and Wales, where the demand was more varied, specialisation began during training. Because of the dense nature of Scottish forests and the consequent scarcity of lodgings most Scottish Timber Corps girls lived in hutted camps in the heart of the woods. Girls working in England, on the other hand, normally lived in private billets. Large country houses were taken over for training where for a month the theory and practice of forestry were taught – felling, cross-cutting, 'snedding' or lopping off the side branches, drawing the trunks out with horses and tractors, working sawmills, loading and stacking pit props. After one week of general instruction girls were allocated to whatever branch of timber production they had chosen.

Attempts were made to look after the welfare of Timber Corps girls, in the same way as the rep looked after the land girl. The central office of the Ministry of Supply in Bristol employed women officers specially trained in dealing with welfare problems, but despite this many English Timber Corps girls seem to have had a raw deal on lodgings and a shamefully inadequate diet. Betty Gingill, who joined the Women's Timber Corps as a seventeen-year-old and worked in Wiltshire was not served one hot meal from December to March. 'There were three of us. We used to say, "bread and pepper today for dinner." Once one of the girls was so hungry she ate writing paper. The Italian prisoners of war saw how hungry we were and used to give us the few bits of dried fruit that was doled out to them as part of their lunch. We had inadequate bedding at night. The mattress was two inches thick, you could read a newspaper through the blanket. We used to put the bedside rugs over us to try to keep warm.'

Monica Robinson encountered the same gradgrind mentality among her landladies. 'In one billet we returned to bread and dripping for the main meal – having lifted heavy timber all day; at another scrambled egg, made from reconstituted egg powder . . . At night we froze. Two cotton eiderdowns covered the bed; one fat and one thin. We dressed fully to get into bed, carefully placing an overcoat and a threadbare rug from the floor on top of the eiderdowns.'

A member of the Women's Timber Corps felling a tree, possibly in Angus, between 1943-5.

Strength and suppleness were vital to combat stiffness and aching muscles that wielding unfamiliar heavy tools brought with it and the day at training camps began outside at 6 a.m. with exercises designed to strengthen the muscles used in axe swinging.

The Timber Corps girls were obviously admired by the public. A Scottish newspaper, describing a parade celebrating the first birthday of the Women's Timber Corps, reported:

Crowds of people thronged the streets of Inverness on Saturday afternoon and witnessed a parade of timber girls who are engaged in tree-felling operations in the Highland area . . . Wearing their attractive uniform, consisting of khaki breeches, green pullovers, and jaunty green berets, the girls paraded on Bank Street, where the spectators had an opportunity of admiring the precision with which they carried out drill movements preparatory to marching away. They were led away by the pipers and drummers of the Highland Squadron of the Air Training Corps . . . and the selection of pipe tune 'Highland Laddie' was not inappropriate considering that although not Highland 'laddies' the timber girls are doing men's work.

Women's Timber Corps work offered a considerable variety of tasks. Some girls worked in the forest itself, measuring, felling, snedding and hauling the timber, turning the unwanted branches into huge cheering bonfires. Others worked in the sawmills, a job, like threshing, notorious for its accidents. Vita Sackville-West particularly admired the girls who worked in the mills: 'This is a terrifying task, as anyone who has watched the great toothed circular saws whirring with murderous speed will agree. It is a task which requires extreme care, precision and concentration, for the saw which will travel with prolonged and undeviating ruthlessness up the solid trunk of wood will slice in one second through the soft finger, the pulsating wrist . . . Men have been known to shake their heads and say no, it didn't take their fancy; but the girls of the Timber Corps have done it.'

In fact the only deaths that occurred in the Women's Timber Corps were due more to an act of God than to deadly machinery. In July 1944 two Timber Corps girls in Dumfriesshire were killed when the timber wagon they were travelling in, pulled by a tractor, overturned and crushed them.

Taken with kind permission of the author, Nicola Tyrer, from "They Fought in the Fields'.

———◆———

"We heard the air raids in Aberdeen. There was the blackout and the skylights were covered with bags. We carried the lanterns to the steading in bags."

———◆———

"The younger generation has no idea how people worked. You got your pockets full of water and your boots used to freeze bone hard in the morning."

THE BOTHY IN KILMUN

John Rennie

We were a pretty mixed bunch, meeting on the steamer for Kilmun at Gourock, recruited in the palatial office of the Forestry Commission in West Nile Street, Glasgow.

I do not know the reason why the others accepted the job of forestry worker, but my wish was for a job in the fresh air after six years in factory work, and the prospect of a chance of a Forester's course after a six month probation spell at Benmore. The winter of 1947/48 was the most severe in living memory, the frost lifting the road surfaces in Argyll after thawing by six inches, and splitting tree trunks.

There were six of us, met by the Benmore Head Forester, a John Watt, I think, and taken a few hundred yards to the Bothy from the pier, after the cook, self appointed, collected our ration cards to prepare the evening meal. Since he used our entire margarine ration to make spam and chips we were not impressed by his efforts, so after a week or so he was reduced to the ranks and a chef sent from Glasgow. Well, he said he was a chef, prior to war service with the Eighth Army as a cook.

Jimmy Brown was a great character, somewhat bomb-happy after being chased by Rommel across the North African desert. He had survived a mortar attack on his six ton truck, but his pots and pans were scattered over the desert. Gone too were his savings, kept in an old ammunition box, and carefully hoarded from the sale of empty bottles (and no doubt bully beef) to the Arabs.

Since it was spring we started in the nursery, steam cleaning the soil, planting seedlings, hoeing weeds, digging new seed beds, an easy introduction to honest toil. As I was well used to hard work no problem, but some of the younger boys from the town used to fall asleep while dining at night as the fresh air and sore muscles took their toll.

The bothy consistied of 3 areas; cook-house, store, dining hall. And the sleeping hut, fitted for twenty inhabitants with toilets, showers, boiler-house, and a separate section for the cook. The compound was surrounded by a high hedge and next to a disused tennis court was a chalet occupied by Timber Aggie and her father, employed in dragging felled timber from the hillside. To see Aggie handle the horses and awkward loads was a revelation to our town-bred eyes.

We were picked up each morning by lorry and driven round the Holy Loch to Kirn picking up local staff. We passed Robertson's and Morris & Lorimer's Boatyards, both with full order books after wartime, in those happy days when yachts were built by craftsmen of sweet smelling wood.

On the loch the American team, competing for the Seawanacka Cup, were practicing light weather sailing night and morning, but in vain, as the local helmsman, Herbert Thom, winner of at least six hundred races, sailed rings round them.

One new recruit was a six foot two inch Rhodesian, John Young, whose father had come from Glasgow, migrated to East Africa, and opened a large store in Umtali, Rhodesia. His first venture in setting up a store was near a river crossing on the veldt on a wide well-trodden track, on an assurance by the natives of heavy traffic on the track. There must have been a language problem, for the heavy traffic was of elephant herds, and the Young family endured never-ending footsteps as the herds tramped to traditional feeding grounds, six months one way, six months the other way.

John Young had spent most of the war years as a cadet on the barque Lawhill, built in

Aberdeen, but German owned. She was impounded by the South African War Department and skippered by a veteran Finnish sailing ship-master; crewed by cadets she sailed between Africa and Australia with a cargo of grain, well out of shipping routes and enemy submarines.

When John decided to visit Scotland he signed up on a cargo boat as a stoker, easy as some of the Liverpool-Irish stokehold crew either deserted or were jailed in Capetown.

As the stokers and trimmers were a pretty rough lot John's gear was stolen the first night on watch, but he was hard as nails, and by working as hard as they did he was accepted as one of the stokehold and his gear was returned bit by bit before docking at Liverpool. One of the crew, who had given his wife most of the passage money from a previous voyage, described her with her new clothes, in admiration, as looking like a first class whore.

John, at 22 years, was as daft as a halfpenny brush, with no fears or inhibitions. He smoked thick black tobacco in brown paper and when drunk often stripped naked and would run past a nearby convalescent home for women to the screams of outrage or delight of the patients. When John's family eventually found out where he was they sent money for his passage home, but as John spent it his sister was sent up from London to escort him back. Sadly I never kept in touch with him.

We always seemed to attract odd bods. One, who claimed gypsy blood, acted so strangely we had doubts about his sanity, and when he bought a dinghy, took it down to the beach and sawed it into ten pieces, we were not surprised when he was taken to Lochgilphead.

There were two more from overseas, an Anglo-Burmese, Tom MacEachran, whose father had worked for a tin mine in Burma. He was forced to flee with wife, daughter and two sons to the Indian border when the Japs invaded Burma. Only the father and sons reached India, one son to join the Indian Army, the father and younger son coming home to Scotland.

The other, whose name I have forgotten, came from Argentina, and was forced out when the government nationalised the railways, mainly run by Scots. His father had the idea that chopping down trees might reverse the soft upbringing the boy had been used to in the Argentine, but the boy, aged twenty, declared he was only interested in designing women's clothing. He looked strange on his first day at work, as his dad had a pair of expensive boots made for him, asking his son to give him a tracing of his foot size for the bootmaker; but the boy gave him a tracing of his shoe and the finished boots looked like a pantomine prop. His inability to do even simple tasks at work meant a swift return home, which he probably intended anyway.

There were no power saws in those days, and as the crosscurt saws needed two to operate them, I was paired with what seemed to my callow eyes a small old man. Was I mistaken! He was the hardest worker I have ever come across, and as we were on piecework felling at 4d per tree, I did not straighten my back all day. He was a St. Kildan, one of those evacuated in the thirties from the island at the Islanders request, and given Forestry cottages and jobs.

That was 4d a tree, 2d each, and with luck I could make £5.00 each week against the standard Agricultural wage of £4.00, paid in an army-style pay parade every fortnight in Benmore Nursery.

We spent most of that very hot summer thinning out the forest on west Loch Eck, dragging the felled trees to above the road. We laid a heavy wire rope round a big boulder on the hill slope and anchored the other end round a tree next to the road. We hitched up some trees with a wire sling and pulleys sent the load down the wire. Luckily no-one was killed as the load hit the road, shattering on impact. No Health and Safety Legislation in those days! The next loads had a drag wire attached to slow the descent and to retrieve the pulleys each trip, though it was hard slow work hauling up.

One other chore we had, I suspect a punishment job, was to load stobs in the creosote tank, pump the creosote out of the holding drums with a leaky hand pump, and fire the boiler to heat the creosote. Even after several showers you still smelled all week.

We moved round to Glen Masson, cleaning out the ditches dug on the hillside and planting with Sitka Spruce, the gang strung out six feet apart planting backwards downhill. Two new horses carried the seedlings up the hill, but when the rain got heavy were taken back to the stables. As we were left in the rain to carry the bags of seedlings uphill I complained to the Forester, to be told that the horses were valuable, cost money, and we came free.

One job we did was to remove an old oak tree leaning over the Kilmun Graveyard, a very awkward job supervised by one of the gangers, the manual labour done by the bothy squad. As the tannic acid sap was running in the oak we went back to the bothy looking like Picts covered in blue dye from the reaction on the steel tools.

At the summer's end I discovered there were six hundred applicants for forty places at Forestry College and that foresters' sons had automatic entry. I realised I had been conned and left, as at four pounds a week (mainly spent in the Cothouse Inn) I could not afford to work at forestry, though probably the healthiest and most enjoyable job I have had.

(Courtesy of Forest Life Picture Library)

"My father brought fat cattle over from Derry to Glasgow. It took six or seven hours to transport them and cost 1/- a head. The conditions on the boat were pretty cramped but it must have been worth it. When he got there he was told that it was a bad market – there was a good load of Canadian cattle. It would be useless to sell them. He went to bed miserable that night but in the morning they told him there was something wrong with the Canadian ones and they had to go into quarantine. He was in luck, his were the only ones in the market that day and he got a tremendous price for them."

73

Rural Reminiscences
6. Domestic Life on an Aberdeenshire Farm
Circa 1932

"My mother was the youngest in the family by a long way. She desperately wanted to be a nurse but one had to pay for their learning plus work in the wards and Granda said farmers' daughters didn't go out to work, they stayed on the farm until they were wed. My father was a photographer but the recession and the First World War ended his career in photography.

My Aunt Liz (older by many years) and her husband farmed beside Mains (where my grandparents were) and a brother next to them so there were three farms we could visit. Aunt Liz and Uncle Willie had no children and I usually visited them.

I wonder if anyone recalls having to fill their mattress "tike" with freshly threshed chaff before they got into bed? Aunt and I went to the indoor thresher and I held as she scooped in the sweet smelling chaff. It was not unlike the present day duvet but bulkier and it was a climb to get into bed and feel the mattress mould to your body. No hot water bottle, a brick was put in the oven every morning and it was wrapped in flannel and placed in the bed. Hard but cosy.

The men employed on the farm slept in the bothy, which was cleaned by my Aunt, and they were fed in the kitchen. Water and towels was set out for them to wash their hands. The food was on the Dover Stove and the Grieve sat at the top of the table and then the others by seniority and they were served accordingly. I was never allowed near the kitchen when the men were at meals. Our food was sent "ben the hoose" prior to the workers coming in.

Cheese was made by my aunt and I can visualise rows of round white cheeses wrapped in muslin. Butter and eggs were sold to the grocer and groceries were bought by a barter system.

The first washing machine I ever saw was at my Aunt's. It was an Acme. A paddle shape inside was powered by elbow grease by turning a handle a half turn and back. Before one could use it of course, water was carried to the boiler which we kept stoking until we had an ample supply of hot water to use in the machine. To drain off the water there was a tap at the base. Having filled it with a bucket, it was emptied by bucket – no waste! This soapy water was then used to scrub the corridor and the flag stoned kitchen and right out to the back door.

Life on the farm was routine. A day was set aside for the washing, another day for the butter and cleaning and boxing eggs and a third for baking. As I recall, the girdle was used far more than the oven. We made girdle scones, oatcakes and pancakes and this reminds me of the warm harvesting days when Aunt would carry the copper kettle full of hot tea and I carried the baskets of butter scones and pancakes out to the men. Cheese and oatcakes were always served at the table. Oatcakes were eaten with every meal, having been baked on the girdle, toasted on the toaster hooked in front of the fire and then cooled. The oatcakes, so easily broken, were stored in the meal girnel.

Another memory I have is of peats. A stack of peats was set up for winter fuel. Peat cutting was back breaking and time consuming work; cut, set to dry and then built onto a cart and taken to the farm from the peat bog, but oh the smell of the peat fire! It was dusty but not as dirty as coal.

Whilst Uncle Willie and Aunt Liz's farm was grain and cattle, Uncle William was a

Bothy boys at the Rhynd, Leuchars, Fife. L-R, Tom Balfour, Jim Henderson, Will Sneddon, Jimmy Berry, Bob Donaldson. The men created these caricatures of bothy life for fun, but also as a record to keep of those they had worked with, as they were liable to move to a different fee at the end of the six-month term.

sheep farmer and at his farm I can visualise the sheep being dipped and the shearing. As children, at the end of clipping we were given the task of collecting all the daggings. We each had a tub which we filled with water from the burn to soak them. The first wash of water was used for feeding the garden. We swished and played with a stick to move the wool around, constantly changing the water until we were given the "all clean" signal. The wool was then hand squeezed and spread out on an old blanket or sheet to dry.

It was then sent on to my grandmother and Aunt Ina (who looked after my grandparents) and so began the spinning of the wool. First it was oiled with "sweet oil" (I've never found out what kind of oil that was, it looked like olive oil) then it was carded. I can see my Aunt laying the wool on the carder and taking a second one to brush it, carrying out this movement from one to the other until she could roll off a ringlet of wool. It looked so beautiful lying by the side of the spinning wheel. It looked so easy watching the wheel set in motion, each ringlet rolled and pulled gently onto the preceding one.

Socks and balaclavas were knitted on wires (steel needles) but when it came to sweaters we had another task in store, dyeing. Heather roots were boiled to give an earthy brown colour – mooret as my Aunt called it. The yellow was the flower of the gorse and green a plant in the garden, unfortunately I cannot recall which one. It was a lovely sight to see the wool, now dyed, in the hanks, hanging on the ropes to dry. Such changes in the clothing from my childhood to the present day. Vests, underwear, stockings and socks were all knitted from the daggings. My one regret is that I didn't keep one piece of it.

Underwear and pillowcases were bleached in the sun, these items having been made from flour sacks. I can recall the baker selling the empty sacks which were opened up flat and washed and bleached in the sun. Flannel was also another material used for underwear. Gents wore flannel above the vest.

Sugar sacks cost 6d and were used to make clootie rugs. Many households spent winter evenings hooking a clootie rug. Each had their own designs. They were warm but oh so dusty! Nothing was wasted. Outgrown clothing etc was used to make the rugs.

Spring cleaning was an arduous task for a 10-12 year old. The blankets were tramped in the wash tub, mattress trailed out and aired, carpets flung over a strong rope and beaten and the polish was made from beeswax or shellac and turpentine and required a lot of elbow grease. Fire-places were polished with black lead, the steel parts scoured with emery paper. The fender was brass and very ornate – I think Brasso was used for polishing this.

I can still visualise Mrs Hay, a well built lady dressed in the rig-out fisher women wore in that era – a dress and striped apron. She travelled by bus from Peterhead to Ellon every week with a large creel on her back, held in place by a strap that crossed over her chest, and a basket on each elbow. She went round the village selling dried fish which the farmers stored for winter and in the herring season a barrel or pail was filled with herrings and salted to keep them all winter. I remember my mother's pail of salted herring. The fish were removed the night before eating, soaked then rinsed and laid on top of the pot of potatoes. As the potatoes cooked, so did the fish. No salt was added. They were carefully lifted out and the potatoes drained and mashed. Turnips or carrots were served with them and these had been pitted to keep frost free. A feast fit for a king; herring, mashed potato and turnips. The dried fish was soaked perhaps two nights. They were huge flat fish and a portion was cut off after soaking and rinsing. Cooked in the same way as the herring, they were mashed through the spuds with a piece of butter and spoon of cream whipped in. This delicacy was known as "Hairy Wullie" because the fish flakes looked like hair amid the potatoes. The veg could have been cabbage or any veg that stood the winter.

Curly kale was boiled with a good marrow bone added to the water – you could buy one from the butcher for 2d. The kale was removed from the water when cooked and the water brought to boiling point and used to make brose for breakfast. The kale bree flavoured with the bone was stirred into oatmeal, salt and pepper.

Sowens was another dish that was used as a supper meal. I recall collecting the small seeds of grain that was the basis of sowens from a meal mill. The lady had them soaked, we carried them home in a flagon and they were cooked like porridge but looked greyish in colour. Fruit was bottled, gooseberries and rhubarb are two I recall. Apples were dried in the oven in rings but, kept frost free they could be stored. Jam was usually made totalling 1lb for each day of the year. This allowed for jam tarts and copious "pieces" in the field during harvest.

A ham would hang above the fire-place when a few farmers went together and killed a pig. Each shared in the killing of the pig. To make mealy pudding, the intestines were cleaned beyond all measure, suet, meal, onions, salt and pepper pushed in and tied off then cooked. If we were helpful we would get a little pudding as a reward. It was a lot of work.

Food was preserved in the land by means of a pit. Potatoes, carrots, cabbage, beetroot, covered in straw, sometimes sacking and old rugs, masses of earth to keep the frost out.

The finale of harvest was the "Meal and Ale". I can visualise sheaves decorating the barn. Two sheaves in the X shape hung up all around. The loft area was left clear for the gramophone complete with horn and the drinks, ginger beer for wee gate-crashers like myself and cousins.

Food in abundance from stovies to clootie dumpling. The drink handed out to the grown-ups who had walked or cycled from far and near – I never found out what they were given. The dancing was square or waltzes, popular at that time. Entertainment was provided by anyone who could play the melodeon, mouth organ, Jews harp, bagpipes and of course bothy ballads. Such a jovial time and through the eyes of a youngster a fantastic experience and one that everyone enjoyed. The joy of farming was the seasons, Spring, Summer, Autumn and Winter. Each had their own dawning and all different.

Happy care-free days with summers that always seemed to be warm. An atmosphere of friendliness, help thy neighbour, that sadly seems to be disappearing in some sections of society. Can it be our clamour for material things?"

———

"My father brought speaned calves back from Skye. They turned out to be grand calves just ready for the market. They had to go away from Skye because there was no keep to feed them. I think my father and his friends always told the same stories which is why I mind about them."

Rural Reminiscences
7. The Horror of Foot and Mouth Disease in Orkney

"In autumn 1960 foot and mouth disease in animals found its way to our islands. It had never reached us before which meant everybody was afraid of it and had no idea what to look out for. All ideas were listened to as symptoms were discussed. The disease was darting from one parish to another so fast we surmised that all farms in the end would be wiped out. The school attendant at the school our family attended got it at his farm. The teacher advised pupils whose parents were in farming to keep their children at home until the all clear was given. We kept our children at home, we stayed at home, all grocery vans, mail vans, all outside transport and visitors were advised to stay away. Nothing had been coming in or going out for two weeks.

On 6th December 1960 we went out to do the morning feeding of cattle and sheep to discover one breeding cow was unhappy at moving over but was eating normally and it seemed she had perhaps slipped and twisted her ankle. We went inside to have our own breakfast before cleaning the byre.

That cow seemed more lame by dinner-time. We decided to call in the vet. It was a ministry vet who arrived. He looked in her mouth and scraped on her tongue to reveal a small bit of skin lifting. He then lifted up the lame leg and scraped between the cloves which also showed signs of tender skin. He left it for a short time then checked again when he was able to confirm another case of foot and mouth. He set the wheels in motion and by 5pm that night the digger had dug a massive grave near our house. The children being so young they did not understand what was going on and we decided to pull the curtains and turn up the TV loud to muffle the sound of shooting and we would leave the vets to carry on with the disposing and we would stay inside. Soon after we made our plans a knock came to the door, a vet asking if my husband would help them and lead out the animals to the place of slaughter as they knew him and would follow him better. He was very reluctant to do it but gave in but it left him very upset and unable to sleep for quite a while.

I hoped I would be spared the agony of seeing our stock wiped out but that was not to be. The Department of Agriculture office always phoned up and asked me to go and get a ministry vet in to speak to them. It was really a nightmare having to go to the graveside where the digger was pulling cattle into the grave and others were being shot on sight. I had to go on that errand quite a few times and call the vet to the phone! Instead of my husband and myself keeping clear of the ordeal, we had to be very much involved which was most distressing.

The two weeks which followed was taken up by a team of men employed to clean out and disinfect the outbuildings, our work clothes etc as well as burning all contact with the animals such as ropes, feeding stuffs, wood or anything involved.

We were all in quarantine for six weeks, in all we had been tied to the farm for two months. Luckily this was the last case. We spread it to nobody and by February 1961 we got the all clear to restock. The prices we had to pay far outstretched the compensation we got for restocking. Also it took years to get the cattle back to the standard of the ones we lost."

FOOT NOTE. "*Foot and Mouth was very distressful and a blow to whoever got it but nothing compared to this world ban on British beef with store cattle down £100 per head at the moment, no farmer can carry on no matter how good he is.*"

FISH FARMING IN SCOTLAND

Dr. Ron Roberts

Fish Farming is the Cinderella of Agriculture, but she very much wears a tartan ballgown. The very first fish farmers were the Chinese and the Egyptians. Their vases and bas reliefs, clearly showing fish cages and ponds date back 5000 years and more. Moses indeed threatened the Pharaohs not only with plagues on cattle, crops and first born, but he also threatened the destruction of the fish cages on the Nile (Isaiah 19 verse 10). The fish involved was the Nile tilapia, <u>Oreochromis niloticus,</u> the fish that fed the five thousand at Capernaum and also provided the draft of fishes. Now it is farmed not only in Israel and Asis but even in Scotland in heated water from industrial processes and appears on supermarket slabs as St. Peter's fish.

Fish farming in Scotland, however, is synonymous with salmon and trout. The Atlantic salmon, our native salmon, is a palearctic fish, not found in the Southern hemisphere, which fits exactly into the ecological niche which our cool temperatures and clean Atlantic waters provide for it.

Salmon farming began with the discovery by James Shaw of Drumlanrig in 1839 that parr, the young stages of salmon–small, brown and undistinguished little fish found in freshwater–were the same species as the large silver salmon coming up from the sea each autumn to spawn. This led to the Stewartfield experiment on the Mansefield estates at Scone, showing that salmon could be reared artificially and even transferred to salt water. This was the first example of salmon farming in history.

All of these studies were aimed at improving wild stocks. The father of modern scientific aquaculture, Sir James Maitland of Sauchieburn and Barnton, was also interested in this, the improvement of sport fisheries in lakes and rivers, but his writings and his practical experiments, which survive to this day have been the basis for food fish farming now practised through the world. Maitland's book, <u>The History of Howietown,</u> was published in 1887, and copies of it are still in great demand in the antiquarian book trade. He had an enthusiasm for his mission – to show that fish could be farmed in the same fashion as cattle and sheep, but he was determined that his efforts should be conducted in a scientific and reproducible fashion. He was so successful that his hatchery and farm at Howietoun, near Bannockburn, still operates profitably, over a century after its establishment.

Howietoun brown trout and salmon fry were distributed throughout the UK, and provided sport fisheries with a service second to none, but much more significant was the role Maitland played in distributing salmon and trout eggs around the world. Descendants of Howietoun trout, still occur in the Kenya Highlands, the Southern Ghats of India, Tasmania, Canada, USA, Falkland Islands and South Africa. His stock, particularly his strain of brown trout derived from Loch Leven and local feral strains, was renowned for its sporting qualities.

Farming of salmon and trout for food, rather than sport was a much newer development. Trout farming was principally carried out using the fast growing rainbow trout – a native of the Western US, rather than the slower growing brown trout. The pioneers of this industry were the Danes, who established in Southern Jutland an extensive trout industry based on agricultural co-operative marketing principals, using earth ponds and feeding the trout on trash sea fish.

This industry had grown significantly by the 1960's, when two Scottish farmers, independently decided to try to transfer the technology to Scotland, and become Scotland's first commercial food fish farmers. David Brien was a young poultry farmer at Almondbank, and he, with the help of Drummond Sedgwick, the Inspector of Salmon Fisheries, set up a Danish-type pond farm using the mill lade of a disused grain mill on the Almond.

Graeme Gordon, laird of Kenmure, had just returned from Africa, where he had worked for a spell after serving in the SAS in Malaya. He decided to try to rehabilitate the family lands at New Galloway, but was not sure how to do so. He had seen the trout farms in his wife's native Denmark, but there was no flowing water of significance on his lands. He decided to set up a totally new, pumped water, farming system, using water from Loch Ken, distributing it through a system of canals into ponds in low lying land around the loch.

Fortunately, both were successful and by 1970 they had influenced and inspired a whole new industry, principally in the borders area. In Argyll Kames Fish Farming was to revolutionise trout culture by their innovative cage system, now exported from Argyll to all four corners of the world.

Yet another export was the Kenmure system to England, where the Earl of Radnor adapted redundant water meadows to form the largest trout farm in Europe.

It was in the mid 1960's that salmon farming for food also began, this time however, it was not translated from Scandinavia, but very much an indigenous technology. It did though build not only on the work of Maitland but also on restocking technologies devised in Sweden and Canada to restock rivers with young salmon from hatcheries, where hydro-electric schemes had prevented adequate natural spawning and recruitment.

The guiding light in the pioneering development of salmon farming in Scotland was a small, but very dynamic, division of the multinational company Unilever. This was the second effort this company had made at the revolutionising of Scottish fisheries. Lord Leverhulme, its founder, had spent a great deal of money, to very little avail, in trying to establish a major fishing industry in Lewis in the 1920's. Fortunately, there was very little corporate memory of this fiasco in the Unilever of 1965, and the company established a development facility at Lochailort, in Invernessshire, which enjoyed the back-up of the whole Unilever Research organisation. Once they had shown that an industry based on farmed salmon was feasible, they set up a production company, Marine Harvest, which is now an independent multinational in its own right. Marine Harvest-McConnel is the largest fish farming company in the world, with major operations in Chile as well as Scotland, but all operated from a world headquarters at Craigcrook Castle in Edinburgh; it is a fine example of a large Scottish company developed by linking Scottish business and scientific skills to a commerical end.

At the same time as the Lochailort experiments were going on, two Norwegians, the Vik brothers, were independently attempting to farm salmon in the Sundalfiord. Their efforts were hampered by lack of capital and access to the research base which the Unilever scientists could command, but the conditions in the Norwegian fiords were in many ways more conducive to salmon culture than the stormy waters of the West of Scotland. Norwegian salmon were also much larger, in the wild, than Scottish, so they formed a much better foundation stock.

Once the basis for an industry was established, in both Scotland and Norway, governments readily saw the potential it had for development in the rural, economically disadvantaged, western coastal fringes of their respective countries. In Scotland, the Highlands and Islands Development Board, under its distinguished Chairman, Sir Kenneth Alexander, began a bold and very successful development plan using aquaculture as the engine of economic growth for whole sectors of coastline in some of the more deprived

The past: grading young trout by hand, 1918. The fish were then carried in the metal canisters by pony and pannier to stock hill lochs or rivers. (Courtesy Professor Ron Roberts)

The future? 'Cruive' fish cages in Loch Fyne. Designed for severe locations offshore, remote from a shore base, the cages are 45m square, and each of the four nets can hold 125 tonnes of fish. The building houses a 75 tonne store for computer controlled feeding, office, operators mess and machinery. (Courtesy of Lithgow Aqua Services)

areas. Not least of these was the Outer Hebrides, where Lord Leverhulme had come so spectacularly to grief; there is now a thriving salmon farming industry, schools are full of young Gaels whose parents work on or manage the farms, and the whole infrastructure of many dying crofting communities has been transformed.

In Norway, salmon farming got off to a more hesitant start because of the lack of infrastructure and the economically naive, however altruistic, Government policy of insisting on a maximum size for farm site concessions. This was socially desirable in terms of allowing as many independent producers as possible to establish themselves, but as the industry grew, it crippled development.

Once the Norwegian industry was able to shake off these limitations, it was able to use its much more favourable environmental conditions and a very much more supportive Government to grow to almost four times the size of the Scottish industry. Scottish fish farming is nevertheless second only to beef, in terms of economic size, being worth some £200M in direct production sales at farm gate prices. This takes no account of the income derived from feed production, fish processing, marketing and distribution, which makes aquaculture now the largest Scottish agricultural industry in employment terms, employing more people than even the cattle industry.

Salmon farming is divided into two distinct phases, the freshwater stage, where young salmon larvae, hatched in a purpose built hatchery, are reared in tanks to the silver, smolt, stage. Many farms in Scotland still rear smolts in cages in freshwater, but gradually these will be reduced in number as environmental concerns for the effects of the farms on the delicate ecosystem of Highland lochs increase.

Once the salmon in the freshwater farm take on the silver coat of the sea going smolt, usually in April or May, they must be transferred to salt water. Usually, this means transfer to circular or square cages floating in a sheltered sea loch, where they will be fed on carefully formulated pelleted feeds until they reach ten pounds or more and are ready for harvesting. Recently, however, pressure to move further offshore has developed, due to a shortage of sheltered sites for expansion. This has led to innovative approaches to engineering offshore facilities, which can be operated in rough seas. These need to be large and self-contained enough to allow staff to live onboard, or else to operate feeding systems remotely from onshore.

The most distinctive of these is the Cruive system developed by the Lithgow Group. These structures, manufactured at the Campbeltown Shipyard are classified as ships and can hold up to 500 tonnes of growing salmon. Serviced by underwater television monitors, and computerised feeding systems, they are the prototypes for a whole new generation of offshore technologies which will allow not only salmon but all aspects of aquaculture to develop in the wider expanses offshore. This will help this innovative new industry, which is only now reaching the levels of technology commonplace in terrestrial agriculture for years, to take its place in feeding the world.

The farming of fish has only been possible in Scotland because of the inputs of a number of other skills. Not least of these have been the engineering skills of the cage builders, the netmakers and the specialist shipbuilders. Well-boats, the latterday equivalent of the Clyde puffers, now service farms up and down the coast. Helicopters are widely used to lift precious stocks of young parr and smolts from the hatchery to distant lochs for on-growing. Refrigerated transport lorries allow salmon to be in French and German markets only 36 hours after leaving the loch.

Nor was education and training neglected, with Scottish universities and colleges offering courses from degree level to boathandling.

As with all farmed animals, the threat of disease is an ever present one to the fish farmer, and in the 1960's, there were no salmon vets. Thus, the Nuffield Foundation's decision to establish a veterinary research unit at the new University of Stirling, was visionary in its time. With the support of other bodies such as the Overseas Development Administration, Wellcome Trust and the industry's own Scottish Salmon Growers Association, this unit, now a fully fledged Institute has become the largest and most successful of its kind in the world.

(Editor's Note: *Dr Roberts was largely responsible for establishing Stirling University as a world centre for excellence in aquaculture expertise.*)

The salmon farming industry is very much a Scottish agricultural success story. It is beset by many problems, just like its sister industries, but the lusty young Cinderella has now certainly been to the ball. Generally, she was thought to be a success and we can be proud that once again Scottish skills and expertise in animal production lead the world.

—

"In 1925 my father went to Aberdeen and bought a ram at a sale. It was brought out to Kemnay in a van, you see, and he had his bicycle at Kemnay and he put a halter onto the ram and he hopped onto his bicycle and met the bobby! The bobby said "Hey ye hanna got nae lights"
"Oh", he says, "I don't need no lights. I'm leading the ram." And he came home with it in the dark."

—

"Some folk drove cattle to market but there was always a float round here. You could take sheep in a horse and cart. I walked over the hill carrying a cockerel in a bag but it stuck its spurs out and tore my clothes to pieces."

—

"I started farming with £36 7/-. At school they had a savings bank and we put in 6d and by the time I left school I had about £10."

JEAN

by Fordyce Maxwell

The brown face under an elderly cap was lined and leathery, with brown eyes in a web of wrinkles. A clay pipe was stuck in one corner of the mouth, puffing out small gouts of smoke. The other corner turned up with a half smile. It was a face like a friendly crabapple.

An old sports jacket hung loose on narrow shoulders. Baggy trousers flapped at the ankles of heavy brown boots. The clothes hung and fitted where they touched on a worn body with a bowed back and rough, small hands.

Her name was Jean. She was the tenant of a 70 acre holding which was under for almost everything – under stocked, under capitalised, under cropped, under fertilised. What it wasn't short of were people – Jean, two sisters and two German workers, former prisoners of war – cats, and Red Setters.

When my father got the tenancy of a run-down farm in 1951 where the previous tenant had gone bankrupt, Jean was one of our immediate neighbours. The others were established tenant farmers, owner-occupiers and landowners. There was no doubt in those early years who we had more in common with.

She had worked on farms all her life, finally getting a tenancy in middle age. For some years she ran a small dairy from the cramped yards and buildings. Mame, one of the sisters, a strapping figure in wellingtons and sacking apron, looked after the herd of thickset, shortlegged Red Poll cattle, one of the dual-purpose milk and beef breeds which have all but disappeared.

In summer Mame would walk the small herd through the village to the grazing field beside the railway station. In winter they stayed in the yards. Milk was sold round the village from a pony and trap.

But the dairy herd had gone by the time we arrived in the district and the small farm was struggling. Jean was hard working, but disorganised, kind hearted and a soft touch for some farmers and dealers.

Cattle and sheep grazed her fields for which she never received full payment, and she was palmed off with poor quality stock, cancelling efforts made by more generous neighbours to help her along.

She was also, as the saying of the district went, "aye ahint". Crops were late to go in, late to be harvested, weedy and unthrifty. She had a tractor of sorts, but always believed that horses would make a comeback.

Days were spent raking the countryside to farm sales, buying up horse harnesses and brasses and a large assorted collection of other rubbish which "would come in handy some day."

As a small boy on an autumn afternoon I sat and looked at her, wide eyed, after she had persuaded my father to come in for a cup of tea and discuss the possibility of helping her dehorn some cattle. As he raised the cup a cat climbed on to the table and walked across it in a leisurely way. Jean gently lifted the cat off as father put his cup down untasted.

As he did so, one of the setters appeared under the table and started nuzzling between his legs. He pushed it away. The setter came back. He pushed it away more firmly. Jean was drinking tea and looking into the fire.

When the setter came back a third time father clamped his formidable right hand like a rat-trap on its muzzle and the dog's feet scrabbled frantically on the linoleum.

Jean looked round: "Is that dog alright, Tammy?" she asked, as it gave a muffled howl.

"Fine, Jean," father replied as he let go, watching it accelerate backwards, crash against Jean's chair and then go to stand in a corner and shake its head, squinting down its nose to inspect for damage.

It was tea time for the two German workers and Mame. Another setter and the third sister came in. Cats were arriving from various directions and Jean threw another log on the fire. There was a fullness about the room which became unsettling.

"Have to be going," said father briskly, standing up and walking in one movement. But we paused on the way to the outside world to look at a certificate on the wall. It was for a ploughing championship. Jean smiled and nodded:

"A few years ago now, the East Learmouth championship. More than twenty in it. Horses, of course."

"When did you start working with horses?" father asked.

She laughed. The brown leathery face split to show teeth browned by forty years of pipe smoking.

"When I was just a lassie. Driving a pair of horse and deeing a man's job. And I've been deeing it ever since."

There was a brief silence. From the room there was a steady clink and clatter of knives, forks and cups, but no conversation. We said goodbye and left.

I was never in that house again. By the mid fifties, the law of diminishing returns caught up with her. Jean, her sisters, the German workers, the dogs and the cats went quietly. Undefeated, she got a job milking cows at Coldstream Mains, continuing to provide for the whole menage, minus only one German.

Her impressive collection of horse brasses was, years later, donated to the local museum. It is still there. I saw her occasionally over the years and until she died she seemed almost unchanged from that autumn afternoon we sat in her living room – the same baggy trousers, cropped grey hair, cap, pipe and brown-toothed laugh.

But I hadn't thought of Jean for years until I thought about the work of the RSABI, its great effort to raise more money and the good that money can do. Forty years ago it could have made life a little easier for Jean when she left the farm; forty years on there are still people who deserve help.

Not necessarily like her, because she was a one-off, but people on farms and from farms for whom life hasn't worked out as well as it does for most of us. There is almost certainly one near you.

FOOD FOR THOUGHT – A TASTE OF THINGS TO COME

Phillip Thomas

The Scottish Agricultural College

The British consumer is facing an approaching dilemma, involving matters close to the heart of public concern. How do we reconcile demands for an increasing range and abundance of low-cost, high-quality foodstuffs and for conservation of natural, environmental resources with the public scepticism of the ability of science and technology to make such objectives achievable?

The underlying problem is not entirely new. Science and technology has historically faced difficulties in gaining acceptance. There has often been active opposition from the moral philosophers of the day. However, present day tensions between technological advance and the conservative nature of society have a new feature. By and large, developments in engineering and electronics find ready public acceptance but there is much greater reservation about developments in biology and chemistry, and these are very important in agriculture, food production and the management of natural resources. The inconsistencies and contradictions in public attitudes thus give mixed-messages to industry and commerce, and are very confusing for the politicians and legislators seeking to develop regulatory frameworks designed to reassure the public.

WORLD FOOD SUPPLY

The scale of the challenge facing the world's agriculture is immense. Demographic trends show that within the first three decades of the next century food supplies will need to increase by two to three times to meet the needs of the human population. At the same time there is a world-wide recognition that relatively little new land can be brought into cultivation without serious loss of wildlife habitats. After the Rio Summit on the Environment no one believes that substantial agrarian-land expansion can take place without an international outcry. As a consequence, land areas that are already in agricultural use will need to be more productive than they have been in the past.

A QUESTION OF CHOICE

For rich countries such as Britain one could argue that food supply is "not our problem". Most of the pressure to feed the world's population will fall on countries that are economically less fortunate. Average household expenditure on food in the UK is currently only about 12% of the total family budget, and a shift in spending priorities would go a long way to ensuring that we will always get as much as we want from the world food supply, even if some might consider we are taking an unfair share.

However, if we take the view that we will ensure our food supply through our purchasing power we will need to condition ourselves to ignore food supply problems elsewhere in the world. Also we will need to accept that although we can exert strict controls on home standards of food production, the production of our imported foods is largely beyond our control. And finally, we will need to have confidence that we will be able to maintain our present preferential economic position as a manufacturing and service economy, successfully outsmarting competition from rapidly growing economies elsewhere in the world. These are serious issues which need to be considered.

On a basis of contingency planning, logic dictates that the development of high-technology agriculture in the UK will remain of central importance to the social and economic well-being of the country. But the technologies of the future will be heavily influenced by consumer opinion and by environmental and animal welfare considerations.

SCIENCE BASE

Despite the fact that there have been very large reductions in agricultural research since the early 1980s, the UK retains a sound science base to facilitate innovation and technological development. In Scotland the agricultural science is found mainly in the Scottish Agricultural College (SAC) and the Scottish Agricultural and Biological Research Institutes (SABRI), which are funded in part by the Scottish Office Agriculture, Environment and Fisheries Department (SOAEFD).

This science base ensures not only that research relevant to Scottish problems and conditions is undertaken, but that there is a scientific body which can access relevant work from elsewhere in the world. Science and technology is now very much a global business. It is crucial to have the local expertise to be able to interpret and adapt scientific advances that are taking place in other parts of the world.

As in most fields of endeavour, technologies in agriculture are subject to rapid advance. Old technologies are being discarded or updated to meet modern needs, and new technologies are emerging at an ever increasing pace. There is the all pervasive influence of modern computer-based information systems, and alongside the burgeoning impact of the molecular biology and biotechnology revolution.

UPDATED TECHNOLOGIES

There has been much media focus on the use of pesticides, insecticides and fertilisers because of concerns about their potential contamination of foods and impact on the environment. However, research development over the past few years has allowed the widespread introduction of "integrated management techniques". These depend on improved information and a better understanding of the basic biology of pest and weed problems. This has allowed the development of computer-based systems to predict exactly when, under what conditions and in which combinations agrochemicals should be applied. Satisfactory crop treatment can thus be achieved at very low dose rates, sometimes applications can be reduced by as much as 75% of the recommended level.

Likewise, fertiliser technology has improved providing more slowly released products and more precision both in level and timing of application. The latter are based on the use of computer models, incorporating the relevant details of crop biology and the potential losses nitrogen from the soil into surface water.

An emerging development is "precision farming", a technique allowing the computerised sub-division of fields into small areas by use of satellite-location technology, similar to that seen on the television news during the Gulf War. Using this approach a field can be divided into a series of "small gardens" for cultivation purposes. With information from soil maps and the crop in each "garden", applications of fertilisers or other chemicals can be precisely targeted. They can be applied in just the right amount and in just the right place, to achieve the desired effect but without excess. The dangers of food contamination or environmental damage are thus substantially reduced.

In these examples, technological progress has thus been made through a combination of traditional cultivation and modern, high-technology. Further developments of this type will take place as farms become more computerised, and the opportunities for access to information technology and "expert systems" become commonplace.

BIOTECHNOLOGY

Exciting prospects are also on the way in the area of biotechnology, but these developments need careful explanation and presentation to the public. Some of the new technologies, such as the application of enzymes to replace chemicals are fairly familiar concepts because of enzyme washing powders and the like. Similarly, *in vitro* fertilisation and embryo transfer in animal breeding poses few public issues, since the same techniques are used in human fertility treatment.

However, there is a little less public confidence about the molecular technologies, whereby plants or animals with unique characteristics can be produced by manipulation of the composition of their DNA. Nonetheless, this "genetic manipulation" presents mankind with an enormously powerful tool, and offers the potential to transform many aspects of agriculture.

Even now the impact of the technology is beginning to be felt. Genetically modified tomato products have been in the shops for some time, and products made from genetically changed soya bean and maize have recently been licensed. Similarly, in the dairy sector some products are being manufactured using enzyme preparations produced from genetically modified bacteria, rather than being extracted from animals, as was traditionally the case.

But this is only a fraction of what could emerge. At the research level there are already examples of manipulated plants, which have resistance against pests, and reduce the need for pesticides. There are plants that can be manipulated to produce 'industrial' plastic-like products, and there are plants that can be engineered to produce high-cost pharmaceutical products that at present are produced by laboratory synthesis. Likewise, under development are sheep and cows which have been genetically modified to produce in their milk pharmaceutical proteins for the treatment of specific clinical disorders. This offers an enormous potential to increase the availability and reduce the cost of pharmaceuticals on the world market.

Almost no objective seems to be beyond the scope of influence of the new techniques. But the time scale of developments may be longer than many people anticipate, because of the very stringent testing and approval procedures that have been put in place. These are designed to ensure that every development is fully evaluated before it is allowed onto the market.

APPROACHING DILEMMA

Public confidence in such developments is of course a crucial matter. Public information and understanding, and the wider public debate is all important. Unfortunately, the debate presently taking place in many of the Member States of the European Union (EU) is becoming polarised and a perception is developing of a public antithesis to science and technology in agriculture.

This is both damaging and short-sighted. Damaging because there is a very real danger that the EU countries will lose their involvement in the emerging technology, as the multi-national companies decide to locate their research and development in the 75% of the world market that lies outside the EU. Short-sighted because, as highlighted at the start, EU countries cannot isolate themselves from the issues of world food supply and the movement of food across international boundaries. It is therefore only a matter of time before the approaching dilemma will need to be faced.

Rural Reminiscences
8. Berwickshire

"Born in 1912, my childhood was spent on the farm where I grew up. Looking back it was a happy carefree time, playing hide and seek, having horse rides on the horse-drawn bogie long before tractors and modern machinery was invented. It was great fun to us children bringing in the hay. Then in harvest time long carts were used to bring in the sheaves of corn which had been stooked in groups of 8 sheaves per stook and we vied as to who would have the fun of riding on the empty carts as they returned to the field for the next load.

My father was farm steward at that time, the equivalent of farm manager in today's workforce. The farmer himself had no contact with the workers except with my father whose duty it was to give orders to the farm workers, to pay the wages and stamp their insurance cards.

1917. At five years old we children had almost 3 miles to walk to school and the same distance to Sunday school on Sundays. At that time we carried sandwiches to school for our lunch and a tin bottle containing tea which was heated through in the staff room fire.

My father was a member of the school board and one of his duties was to visit the school from time to time to check the register and to discuss with the headmaster the general day to day running of the school. The farm generously provided the bulk of the vegetables for soup, mostly potatoes and turnips. This was a wonderful provision in the cold winter days of the 1920s.

In 1927 my father accepted the offer of the tenancy of a small-holding from the Dept of Agriculture and a move to Berwickshire came about.

Then in 1939 came the second world war when every acre in the country was required in the war effort and 'Dig for Victory' was the encouraging slogan.

In harvest time it was all hands on deck from a university student friend on her vacation to an ex London policeman volunteer. The policeman, who had no experience of farm life whatever caused a stir one day when he dressed up in my late grandfather's black swallow tail coat and his black silk top hat and rode through the village on the tractor in this outfit. This he had unearthed from a cupboard of the bedroom he was occupying in the house. The policeman knew very little about farming but he knew how to enjoy himself.

An outbreak of Foot and Mouth disease affected many farms rather badly. We kept free of this fortunately though our cows were not allowed to cross the public road to reach their grazing field. Because the cows had to come in twice daily for milking they were housed in a courtyard. We were fortunate not to have an outbreak of Foot and Mouth in our dairy herd nor in the vicinity near enough to cause anxiety.

In the years in which we were producing milk for sale very strict regulations were enforced, each month the milk recorder came and stayed over the weekend staying in our farmhouse which was nice for us. Samples of milk were taken over that time and tested for quality etc on a centrifugal machine. This was compulsory. The sanitary inspector also paid visits periodically, inspecting the equipment and everything had to be kept at a very high standard and maintained in the production of milk. It is very satisfying when this can be achieved consistently. Happily we never had a failure.

PS My grandfather had farmed a small farm in bygone days and with pony and trap he delivered his milk in the nearby town dishing the milk straight into the customers' jugs. I wonder how the milk officers and sanitary inspectors would react to that method today?!!

Farm servants at Morphie, Kincardineshire 1903. Top left is the grieve, on the right the shepherd, and bottom right, Mary Lyall, outworker. This picture shows how one farm could be a considerable community.

Rural Reminiscences
9. Memories of our Childhood (Born 1928)

"My brother, sister and I had a wonderful childhood. Our mother was widowed before any of us were at school and we didn't have much but never did without and were very happy. We walked to school and back and would be the first children in the playground. If any of us said we didn't feel well she would say 'By the time you get to school you will be alright.' Some years the three of us would have perfect attendance even though we were soaked many a morning.

As we got up in the morning the lovely smell of oatmeal porridge cooking on a Wellstood stove, and ham and eggs which we got at 7 o'clock. At the forenoon we would get a small bottle of milk to drink with a straw and for dinner it was a bowl of soup and a slice of bread. The lady who cooked the dinner was local and it was made in a boiler and it tasted lovely. Then in later years it had to be someone with more qualifications to make the soup and it never tasted the same.

In the spring we had great fun looking in the hedgerows for the birds' nests. It was great as the eggs would come, then the baby chicks and we'd watch them get feathered and fly off. We would try and see how many kinds of flowers we could see. There was a bakery across from the school and sometimes if we had a penny we could get a poke of broken cakes and that kept us going on the way home. It was quite a long day; left the house about 8 and wasn't home till 5 and on a Sunday we had the Sunday school. Whenever you came in you had to take your school clothes off and into your working clothes and we all had wee jobs to do. Help to feed calves or shut the hens and ducks in or the fox would get them. In a wet night in the spring the ducks would guddle in all the puddles and it took ages to get them to go home. In the morning they weren't allowed out till they had all laid. They all waddled out to the lade for a swim. Once a fox broke into the ducks' house and killed every one but only took one away – left all the rest lying dead in their house. The lade was used for threshing. A slutch was lifted and the water went onto a big wheel that drove the threshing mill. Every Saturday morning it was our job to hand the shaves to be cut and fed into the mill. The straw went down into a shed and one of us was to tramp it as it was being forked up. The corn dropped out of a shoot into the barn loft and then it was shovelled into bags which was fed to the hens and horses and some was taken by horse and cart to the millers to be bruised for the cattle.

In summer when we got our holidays it was hay time. The mower was pulled by 2 horses and then the swaths after a day or so was turned by rakes to dry before being put into ricks. If the weather was bad it was turned several times before it was ready. After the ricks was out for a couple of weeks it was taken into the shed with a rick lift. We loved going out on it and helping to roll the ricks on and if the field was steep a trace horse was needed and we would ride on him. The two main horses were born on the farm and lived till they were 27 years old and was faithful servants.

As we got older we had to learn to hand milk. You had a luggie and a stool. We milked about 45 cows between 5 of us. The milk was sieved into pails then lifted up into a tank and ran down a radiator with cold water going through it and sieved again into 10 gallon cans. The cans were lifted onto a lorry at 7 o'clock by 2 folk and taken to the creamery.

As we went back to school it was harvest time. The binder was drawn by 3 horses and the shaves were then stooked up in neat rows, 6 or 8 to a stook. After the stook was out till dry enough they were brought in to be stacked in the stackyard. The stacks was then thatched and all roped down and lovely clipped to make them look tidy.

Then it was time for the shawing of the turnips and we would help to load the carts also helping to lift the potatoes. At night in the winter we would play cards in a lovely warm kitchen till it was bedtime. We loved every minute of our childhood. We never needed to be scolded and did what we were told. We didn't need a second telling."

Cow, herd and milkmaid with her luggie at the Tail, Crieff, Perthshire about 1900.

THE FUTURE OF RURAL SCOTLAND

Mark Shucksmith and David Gray
Arkleton Centre for Rural Development Research
University of Aberdeen

"I don't know what's going to happen in the next 10 years. Everything is so uncertain now, who knows they could find oil in the Minch and that could completely change everything for everybody. With a major thing like that who knows how far it could go – when big money is offered then you don't know where you are going to stand."

"For the next 3 days I think we'll be okay. I'd like to think that there is a future for them (the children). But as I say everything is so uncertain now. When I first came up (to Wester Ross) I thought 'this is going to be the same for ever more', but it's changed enough in the last 15, 16 years that I know that I can't possibly expect it to stay the same. But I would like to think that it is not going to go downhill."

As these two quotes, from respondents to the study of Disadvantage in Rural Scotland, demonstrate, the mid-1990s are "interesting times", not least for those people and institutions concerned with or working towards alleviating disadvantage and poverty in rural Scotland. While the UK economy continues to grow – providing fresh opportunities in new sectors – social inequalities seem to widen, providing the disadvantaged in the country with unique problems posed by lack of access to well paid jobs and adequate services. There are also societal trends that put increasing pressure on rural welfare institutions. The relative importance of agriculture continues to decline, both in its importance to the rural economy and in terms of the number of people it employs, while alternative economic activity has tended to develop unevenly, generating further disparity. As medical science improves, the general population ages, but in rural areas many young people continue to migrate out in search of broader horizons and better opportunities, leaving an elderly, increasingly dependent population behind.

The 1990s (like the 1980s before) are "interesting times" not least because of the speed at which the institutions, rules and relationships which structure society are changing, as indeed is our experience of life itself. This ephemerality is matched by the need to take an increasingly global perspective on change, with forces emanating from far outside the local arena having significant effects on the lives of those living and working all over rural Scotland. With wider forces impacting on life in rural Scotland, and with many of them in a state of dynamic flux, it is hard to foresee the future of rural Scotland with any certainty. It is possible, though, to consider how and why the world is changing, and how these changes may impact on, and be negotiated by, people in different rural areas and in different circumstances.

FORCES FOR CHANGE

Rural areas of Scotland are subject to major structural changes of unprecedented scale, both as a result of changes in rural economics and societies themselves (eg the decline of agricultural employment) and as a consequence of broader changes in society (eg the role of women) as well as changes in policy at both national and European levels, including the weakening of local government, privatisation and deregulation, tight fiscal controls on government spending, the Maastricht Treaty, the Single European Act, successive reforms of the Common Agricultural Policy, international trade agreements, and the further enlargement of the EU.

In terms of market and economic forces, the declining importance of agriculture and other primary activities and the growth of the service sector is well known. Fewer than 8% of the workforce in rural Scotland are now employed in agriculture, forestry and fishing, compared to 11% in tourism. The service sector, indeed, now makes up more than two-thirds of all jobs in rural Scotland, and its dominance is increasing. Many rural areas are now growing faster than urban districts, while others experience decline : the economic and social processes underlying these diverse trends are not always well understood. One key element is the increasingly global penetration of local markets, with many rural areas and firms seeking to protect themselves from global competition by creating local products which depend on local identity for their market niche. There is a general shift to a service-based economy in which the information and knowledge-based industries play an increasing role, bringing both opportunities and threats to rural areas. These divergent trends are reflected in considerable inter-district variation in unemployment rates within rural Scotland, with the worst affected areas in south-west Scotland and parts of the Highlands and Islands.

Fundamental demographic, social and cultural changes also characterise rural areas of Scotland. An ageing of the population is occurring at the same time as economic restructuring, leading to increased dependency ratios, casualisation and part-time working, and less job security. Migration flows are critical in determining rural population levels, and many people are moving into rural areas because of the new values placed on rural space (eg. clean environment, healthy lifestyles, community life, etc.). Indeed all of the districts in rural Scotland experienced net in-migration between 1981 and 1991. The consequences of the imposition of such new values on rural societies may be far reaching, of course. Many respondents to the Disadvantage in Rural Scotland survey felt that their communities had changed beyond recognition, and that elderly "locals" represented the last repositories of folk memory of an authentic rural past where men and women spent their working lives on the land. Many felt that rural people were losing their culture, language, way of life and identity, and that these intangible qualities were slipping through the hands of their own generation. Social relations are also changing in other ways with the rise of individualist values and the decline of established institutions, such as the Church, perhaps leading to new modes of collective action and solidarity. In the Rural Disadvantage study, women identified themselves as the principal beneficiaries of change, able now to enjoy a less dependent lifestyle whilst maintaining what they described as the positive aspects of rural women's life. They identified more equality in their lives than in the past, and felt that many rural communities revolved around the voluntary and social activities of women.

Rural policies are changing in response to these forces, and many wider policies (especially macroeconomic policies and social policies) also have pervasive impacts on rural areas, as noted above. Further reform of the Common Agricultural Policy is inevitable, in the context of EU enlargement and international trade negotiations, with the certain prospect of declining support to farmers and a shift of resources towards rural development and environmental objectives. The future direction of rural policies was significantly clarified at a recent European conference in Cork, with speeches from the EU Commissioner for Agriculture and Rural Development, as well as several national spokesmen, leading to the issue of a Cork Declaration. It is likely that the structural funds will be reformed, probably becoming more focused and implemented through area programmes specifically addressing rural development goals. The European Commission proposed an integrated rural development policy, applied to all rural areas of Europe but

Steam threshing at Overharden, Lauder, Berwickshire.

A Lanz Bulldog tractor at Whitehill Mains, Musselburgh, East Lothian, 1942.
Tam Hogarth driving, Andrew Knox on the trailer.

sensitive to local contexts, and committed itself to "revitalising rural economies through the adoption of policies designed to promote the development of rural areas taking account of the changing aspirations and priorities of their citizens and the contribution modern technology can make towards the creation of employment.

In Scotland, a rural White Paper, *Rural Scotland : People, Prosperity and Partnership,* was published in December 1995 setting out a similar direction for national policy. Emphasising the themes of partnership and community involvement, the White Paper set out objectives for government policy which will enable rural Scotland to be:

- economically prosperous, with a range of job opportunities which will enable those who live in rural communities, native or newcomer, to enjoy worthwhile ways of life;
- vigorous in its community life supported by good local infrastructure and quality services;
- culturally confident, cherishing local traditions and distinctive ways of life and able to adapt to and benefit from changing circumstances; and
- able to protect, conserve and enhance its outstanding natural environment.

RURAL POVERTY AND EXCLUSION

These trends have different implications for differently situated rural areas (eg remote or accessible) and they will have uneven impacts on different social groups. Several groups face the risk of economic and social exclusion, while others will enjoy new opportunities. The RSABI, with others, recently funded a study of Disadvantage in rural Scotland (Shucksmith, Chapman and Clark 1996), which demonstrated that in rural Scotland "a disproportionate number of the poor are elderly, and a disproportionate number of the elderly are poor". The other main element of rural poverty arises because rural areas contain a disproportionate number of people in low-paid occupations. The land-based industries and tourism are particularly notable in this respect. A third element of rural poverty in Scotland derives from local concentrations of unemployment. Added together, these elements were responsible for 65% of rural households surveyed having incomes below the Low Pay Unit's poverty threshold, and this is a similar proportion to that found in a recent survey by Scottish Homes. Despite such evidence of widespread poverty, however, people's subjective assessment of their welfare tended to contradict such criteria : they compared their situation with the harsher conditions of the past rather than with the current lifestyles of the majority, and therefore did not see themselves as poor nor as entitled to benefits.

Little research has sought to transcend the crude "arithmetic of woe" to explore the processes and system failures lying behind exclusion in a rural context : how do they relate, in particular, to the forces for change discussed above. Evidence from the Scottish study did identify failures in several important systems, though. In terms of civic integration, interviewees spoke consistently about a huge gap between people and policy makers : in the remoter communities a sense of powerlessness was universal, especially in relation to dramatic social changes over which people felt they had no control; in more accessible areas people's sense of powerlessness was closely bound up with social stratification and inequality. Labour market and housing market issues were also crucial, with a majority of respondents perceiving employment opportunities and housing opportunities to be very restricted. Young people and women tended to have the fewest options, and generally jobs tended to be low-paid and insecure. These impediments to economic integration were closely bound up with transport and childcare services, both of which were deficient. The welfare state system was patently failing to reach potential recipients and the take-up of benefits was low. Access to advice in urban centres was problematic, and respondents were often confused about the benefits available and their entitlement. Moreover, their denial of their poverty together with a culture of independence also militated against the receipt of entitlements. Clearly policy innovation is required if civic, economic and social integration is to be achieved in rural Scotland. All of these impacted upon the family and community system, both through a loss of young people which was seen as inhibiting the social reproduction of the community and damaging informal support networks, and through material and social changes which, as we have seen, led to less of a distinctive rural culture, of the Gaelic language and dialects and of a myriad of other intangible qualities.

CHALLENGES AND OPPORTUNITIES

Rural people are not merely the passive recipients of broader forces affecting their lives, and rural development policy has recently placed greater emphasis on enabling and empowering rural people to take greater control over their own destinies through "bottom-up development" approaches that owe much to earlier traditions of community development. At EU level the LEADER programme is a clear instance of this approach, and the Scottish Rural White Paper in 1995 too espoused such an approach. This philosophy is also at the heart of the Cork Declaration, which emphasised the need for capacity-building in rural areas through animation, empowerment and the transfer of technical skills. Such an approach relies on the people of rural Scotland who, it is often said, are our greatest resource. It also requires support and facilitation from government and the voluntary sector.

Inevitably, rapid change and increasing differentiation will continue to characterise rural Scotland in the future. The challenge to rural people will be to exert some control over their own destinies, and over the future of their communities, in the face of these forces for change, enhancing their competitiveness while sustaining their cultures and traditions. The challenge to statutory and non-statutory agents will be to support and enable this process, and to assist those who bear the costs of the adjustment. There are real opportunities, as well as challenges, for rural Scotland in the years ahead. Some people and some areas will gain while others lose, as always in "interesting times".

" Well, Harry, that's got to be the biggest weaner I've ever seen..."

Rural Reminiscences

"We flitted down here (Aberdeenshire) in 1928. Father drove the first horse and cart. It was an old fashioned box cart with wire mesh across it and hens in the bottom. Mother had the horse and gig. There was mother and myself and a box with I don't know how many cats and another box with a clucking hen and another cat in a bag. We drove the cattle and it was a distance of about 12 miles.

There was a white horse at a place beside where I went to school and I well remember that horse. It had a big HD on its side – Highland Division – it was a First World War horse. The owner worked it with a cow.

The prisoners of war went round the farms picking tatties etc in 1944-5. They were mostly Italians at first then Germans. Children from Glasgow were boarded out and came to our school. There were no cars and the blackout and they couldn't see where they were going. Some stayed about a fortnight and some a good bit longer. The teachers came up from Glasgow too.

Quite a few came up and stayed the weekend and left on Wednesday. Still one or two stayed and married but not a lot. One of the teachers came up and the schoolmaster, he was a bachelor and he married her. She still stays near here.

They couldn't believe we could milk cows when milk came in bottles. The road was muddy because it wasn't tarred and they just had shoes, no proper footwear. Some of the local kids were used to walking five miles to school over the hill. They left in the dark and got home in the dark."

———

Geordie Sinclair came down to the market with calves. He had twenty calves in the ring at the same time, all different sizes, and started at £20 and the price got less as the bigger ones were chosen. All I had was £18 and I thought if I got 2 calves at £7 it would cost £14. There were 4 left in the ring and the price had dropped to £6 and I bid and he said "give him the lot" and I only had £18 so I says "No, I can't take them. I haven't the money." But he says:You'll never get a better bargain than that in your life – you take the four calves." I went round to the office with a cheque and I says "What happens here?" So as I came home I stopped at the Bank door and the manager he came out and I says: I've landed a bit of a problem," and he says "what's the problem?"

"Well I've bought these four calves and I can't afford them."

"Have ye nae food for them?" he asked.

"Oh aye, I'm a' right for food." So he said nothing. That £24 never even appeared in the bank book. I never knew what happened. It's changed days now. Well I kept these calves almost two years and then I went back into Aberdeen and I showed them to Geordie Sinclair and I said come and see your calves now. I got £56 for them.

Mr Tom Pettigrew, Mrs Ellen Pettigrew and Miss Elaine Pettigrew